THE MEDITERRANEAN

GREENPEACE
THE·SEAS·OF·EUROPE

THE

MEDITERRANEAN

EDITED BY Xavier Pastor

C&B

First published in Great Britain in 1991
by Collins & Brown Limited
Mercury House
195 Knightsbridge
London SW7 1RE

A CIP catalogue record for this book is available from the British Library

ISBN   1 85585 011 7

GREENPEACE BOOKS
Series Editor: Lesley Riley
Series Co-ordinator: Kieran Fogarty

Picture Research: Philippa Thomson
Index: Jean and Mike Trier

COLLINS & BROWN
General Editor: Gabrielle Townsend
Art Director: Roger Bristow
Design: Bob Gordon
Production: Kate McPhee

Typeset by Lesley Riley and Malcolm MacGarvin
Filmset by The Setting Studio, Newcastle upon Tyne
Reproduction by Scantrans, Singapore
Printed and bound in Italy by New Interlitho SpA, Milan

This book is printed on Hanno'art Pro Matt, a chlorine-free paper
produced by Hannover Papier in Germany.

CONTENTS

INTRODUCTION

T HE MEDITERRANEAN is one of the most beautiful of seas, one of phenomenal richness and variety. But, since the 1960s, the Mediterranean has been appallingly abused. In parts of the north and west, industrial waste is poured directly into the sea, while on the south coast and in the east, many countries striving for development are adopting the very technologies that have been shown to be so damaging in the European countries. Urban waste water is discharged into the sea without any kind of treatment. Oil tankers leave behind them a trail of pollution.

The fishing grounds are relentlessly exploited, while creatures such as the monk seal, the marine turtles and the dolphins are in real danger of disappearing from the sea. The last virgin land is being invaded by developers. The political tensions that have always plagued the Mediterranean are aggravated by the presence of nuclear arms.

The governments of the coastal states, encouraged by the United Nations, have been promising to do something to stop the degeneration of the sea since 1975. But very little has been achieved: some investigations, some agreements over pollution – which are not being fulfilled – promises of co-operation in the event of oil spills, guarantees of protection for small natural areas that, if they are implemented at all, tend to come too late for the endangered species.

It is obvious that the governments of the Mediterranean countries refuse to move from words to actions until they are obliged to do so by the force of popular opinion. Helping to bring this about is the modest aim of this book: to give people information, so that they have the power to demand and achieve changes in political and economic policies. When ordinary people force politicians to act, then there can be real hope for the future of the Mediterranean.

XAVIER PASTOR, PALMA DE MALLORCA, 1991

The Mediterranean – a sea of coral
A bed of red coral (*Corallium rubrum*) provides a rich source of food for juvenile damselfish (*Chromis chromis*). The coral is a vital part of the Mediterranean ecosystem, but much of it has been damaged by trawling gear or stripped from the seabed to be made into jewellery. If the special nature of the Mediterranean is to be preserved, greater protection must be given to the sea and the species within it.

PART

I

The Mediterranean's singular climate is world famous. The region enjoys long, hot summers, and warm wet winters because of the mountains that protect it from the chill of the north and the heat of the southern desert, and because of its distinctive pattern of winds. On the seaward side of the mountains, there is precious little fertile land. The coastal strip represents only 17 percent of the area of the nations bordering the sea, yet it supports nearly 40 percent of their people. The precariousness of life in the Mediterranean is intensified by the sparsity of rivers, especially on the southern coast. Over 90 percent of the water entering the sea from rivers comes from the north. Libya, in contrast, has no perennial river at all.

The Mediterranean is not truly one sea, but several. It is split into distinct regions because of its heavily indented coast, its plethora of islands and because of the deep basins that hollow out its bed. In addition, the life on the sea bottom, in the middle depths, of the surface and of the air form separate yet interdependent communities. Such creatures as the dolphin survive, ultimately, because the fascinating life of the seabed thrives too.

This complex and delicate interaction of geography, climate and natural life is threatened more and more by human activity. Any policies designed to protect the future of the Mediterranean will have to take account of its special character. And that means understanding the region's past: what formed the sea in the first place, and how human history has both adapted to and — to a surprising extent — actually altered the Mediterranean environment.

The inward-looking sea

A satellite photograph, taken looking east from above the Atlantic, makes plain how enclosed the Mediterranean is. The sea loses almost as much of its volume to evaporation as it gains from the Atlantic, from rivers and rainfall — about 95,000 tonnes of water every second. Clearly visible too are the mountains that hem the sea in and so concentrate human activity into a narrow strip along the coast.

THE FACES OF THE SEA

THE MEDITERRANEAN both joins and divides Europe, Asia and Africa, continents as different, in their way, as any on Earth. Yet all life — human, plant and animal — in and around the Mediterranean is conditioned by three things: the mountains that ring its shores, a narrow coastal plain, and the sea itself, dotted with islands. How did this sea evolve, and how, for better or worse, has humanity affected it?

The Mediterranean as we know it is about 5 million years old. It took embryonic form about 20 million years ago, when the long, slow drift of the continents across the face of the Earth brought about the collision between Africa and Eurasia. The initial point of contact was at the western end of what is now the Mediterranean, which was thus closed off from the Atlantic Ocean; the eastern end was still open to the Tethys, a vast, primeval 'world ocean'. Over the next 13 million years, Africa skewed anticlockwise, closing the sea off at the eastern end, while what is now Arabia broke away from Africa, so forming the Red Sea. At the same time, the land on all sides crumpled as the continents pressed together, giving birth to the mountain ranges that ring the sea: the Alps, the Atlas mountains, the Sierra Nevada, the Dinaric alps, the Rhodope mountains and the Taurus range.

The linking strait
The Mediterranean side of the Strait of Gibraltar seen from the space shuttle *Challenger*. The Spanish coast, on the left, and Morocco, on the right, are only 15 kilometres apart; the waters of the strait are just 290 metres deep, whereas the average depth of the Mediterranean is 1.5 kilometres. From this height can be seen the leading wave of the Atlantic current, which refreshes the waters of the Mediterranean at a rate of 1.5 million cubic metres every second. Beneath this influx of water, a current almost as large pours out into the larger ocean. The net gain from the Atlantic is only about 41,000 cubic metres per second.

Vital energy
Smoke and steam rise from a volcano in Sicily. Active volcanoes run in a discernible line across Italy, and an earthquake zone runs along its length. Yugoslavia, the Greek mainland, the Aegean Sea and Turkey also suffer constant seismic activity. This upheaval on the Earth's surface is proof of a more profound movement of the continents themselves, and is a continuation of the slow but massive collision between Africa and Europe that gave birth to the Mediterranean about 20 million years ago.

A prehistoric waterfall

Even once the Mediterranean was formed, it continued to change. Over the next 2 or 3 million years, the enclosed sea evaporated and refilled, perhaps as many as 18 times. The evaporation occurred because the Mediterranean was isolated from the world ocean, and the rivers flowing into it could not replenish the water supply; only a few very salty lakes were left, separated by mountain ranges whose peaks are today's Mediterranean islands.

How the sea refilled each time is so far unknown. Scientists suggest that on some occasions massive storms or earthquakes in the Atlantic could have hurled millions of tonnes of water against the Gibraltar Sill – the lip of rock separating the two seas – gradually breaking down the barrier and allowing the Atlantic to pour in. Over the same period, the level of the sea rose and fell several times as the continents shifted, and this too would have caused flooding. The huge cataract of Atlantic water would have plunged onto the salt desert below at a rate of over 150 cubic kilometres a day, so that the Mediterranean would have taken little more than a century to refill.

About 5 million years ago, a massive earthquake broke down the rocky barrier linking Spain and Morocco sufficiently to make a permanent connection between the two seas. Since then, the Atlantic has continually refreshed the waters of the Mediterranean. Today, the sea still has a high rate of evaporation, and is on average saltier, and denser, than the Atlantic.

So water from the Atlantic flows in, at about 4 km/h, on the surface of the Mediterranean, in a layer between 75 and 300 metres deep. This evaporates, becomes saltier, and sinks, and flows out again into the Atlantic between the Gates of Hercules. It takes at least 80 years for the Mediterranean to renew its water completely in this way. One result of this closed system is that the plankton – the mass of organisms that spend their life drifting in the water – brought in from the Atlantic, which in any other sea would form a nourishing basis for a complex web of interdependent life, is largely washed back out into the greater ocean by the bottom current. Because, too, there are so few rivers bringing life-promoting nutrients into the sea, the marine life is simpler and less plentiful than in other oceans – and the lack of plankton gives the Mediterranean water the sparkling clarity that so many have noted.

Crumpled Earth
The Atlas mountains rise abruptly from the Moroccan desert and show how the land buckled at its edge as Africa ground into Europe between 10 and 20 million years ago, yet left the interior unaffected.

THE BASE OF THE FOOD WEB

Without the plankton – the great mass of minute plants and animals that drift through the water – life in the sea simply would not be the same.

Plant or phytoplankton form the centre of the marine food web. They live in the surface layers, where the sunlight they need for growth is plentiful, and are eaten by copepods (the most numerous of the animal or zooplankton). Copepods, in turn, are food for virtually all the other planktonic animals.

Some of these creatures spend their whole life suspended in the water, drifting with the currents. Others stay there only for their larval stage: the young of worms and barnacles, crabs, shellfish, starfish and sea-urchins will soon take on their adult forms and move to deeper waters or to the seabed. The larvae of many fish also live among the plankton, feeding on ever larger species until they themselves are fully formed and can swim where they choose.

Food for all
Microscopic plant plankton, such as these diatoms (left), use sunlight and minerals to form organic material.

A fine toothcomb
This water flea (*Penilia avirostris*, right) uses its legs to comb the water for food.

Algal grazer
This Mediterranean species of *Eucalanus* (below) is one of the many copepods that feed on phytoplankton.

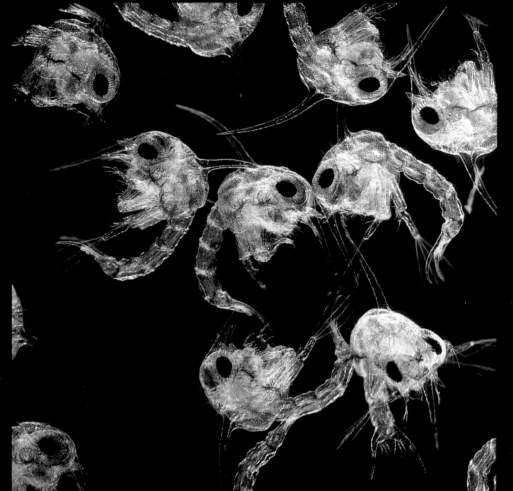

Onward bound
A young squid (*Loligo vulgaris*, above) is on the verge of graduating from the drifting world of the plankton.

Temporary forms
These shrimp-like creatures (left) are larval forms of the shore crab *Carcinus maenas*.

A predatory act
A sea snail (*Ianthina exigua*, below) attacks a Portuguese man-of-war (*Physalia physalis*, to the right). Both float on the surface, the man-of-war by means of its gas-filled 'sail', the snail by a raft of bubbles.

LIFE ON THE BOTTOM

The Mediterranean seabed – of rock, sand or mud – provides habitats for both plants and animals. In shallow water, seaweeds grow on rocky shores; *Posidonia* sea grasses flourish on softer sediments. These plants are eaten by sea-urchins, herbivorous molluscs, fish and even green turtles.

In deeper areas, plants become scarce. Here, bivalve molluscs and animals that are attached to the seabed, such as sponges, anemones, sea fans and soft corals, extract their food from the surrounding water. Among this static life clamber or swim crustaceans, snails and fish. For them the seabed provides shelter from predators or a lair from which to pounce.

Within the sediment, a mass of worms and smaller organisms breaks down the dead material that rains down on the seabed, releasing nutrients that can be carried upwards by the currents, to be used once more by the phytoplankton.

In all of these ways and more the seabed plays a vital part in the entire marine food web.

Key species
The sea grass *Posidonia oceanica* (above) is vital to the Mediterranean, providing habitats and food for many species. Of these, the sea-urchin is the most voracious feeder.

Rocky predator
A member of the whelk family, the triton (below) is a large, warm-water predatory mollusc that feeds on animals too slow to move out of its reach.

Changing nature
The octopus (*Octopus vulgaris*, left) can change colour rapidly to blend in with its surroundings to fool either predator or prey.

Mutual benefits
Sponge crabs (*Dromia personata*, below left) drape themselves with a sponge, perhaps as camouflage. The sponge may share the crab's food.

Burrowing fish
A sand snake eel (*Ophisurus serpens*, bottom left) can grow up to 70 centimetres long. It burrows into sand to stay out of harm's way.

The 'coral' zone
Colonial anemones (orange), sponges (grey and red) and grey-green hydrozoa and bryozoa (sea 'fur' and 'moss' animals) form a dense carpet in the deeper reaches (below).

FISH FROM TOP TO BOTTOM

There may not be a great many fish in the Mediterranean, but there is a rich variety of species. This is partly the result of the varied conditions in the sea. There is a wide range of temperature, such that the water of the northwest is much cooler than that of the east, and different species are drawn to each. Different species favour different depths, too, and the vertical range of the Mediterranean is huge, from the shallow coastal reaches to the deeps of 3,000 metres or more, where no light penetrates and food is scarce. Adjacent seas are another source of species, and fish enter the Mediterranean from the Atlantic and from the Red Sea via the Suez Canal.

The other major reason for the diversity of species is, paradoxically, the relative lack of nutrients in the sea. Phytoplankton and creatures all the way through the food web have such a struggle for food that no single species can dominate the communities living in the various habitats. The many forms of life that result in turn support diversity higher up the web.

Warm-blooded fish
A shoal of bluefin tuna (*Thunnus thynnus*, above) hunts in surface waters. Tuna maintain much of their body at a temperature 10–15°C above that of the water. This allows muscles to deliver three times more power for high speed swimming, a major factor in the success of these predatory fish.

Slim-line predator
John Dory (*Zeus faber*, left) live near the shore. Their bodies are tall but thin: head-on, their profile is reduced to a minimum, which gives them the advantage when stalking their prey. As they get close, they shoot open their jaws and the food is sucked in.

Fearful symmetry
In the Mediterranean the blue shark (*Prionace glauca*, right) grows up to 2.7 metres long and weighs 90 kilograms. Its body is honed for speed, which it needs because its prey are fast-swimming pelagic fish such as mackerel, herring and pilchard, along with the equally speedy squid. Reproduction is also remarkable. Fertilization is internal, preventing the waste of sperm and eggs, and the female gives birth to live young.

Shocking shark

Some rays and skates can generate weak electrical currents using modified muscle cells. The current is used as a sixth sense, detecting objects by the distortions they make in the electrical field surrounding the fish. In the marbled electric ray (*Torpedo marmorata*, right) the electrical organs fill most of the front (pectoral) fins and give a powerful shock, used to stun prey and deter predators.

Illuminating to conceal

Hatchet fish (*Argyropelecus hemigymnus*, left) live in deep, dark water. Their undersides are covered in luminous organs, which break up their outline and prevent them being seen by predators beneath them.

A resident giant

The dusky perch (*Epinethelus guaza*, right) grows to 1.4 metres and lives among rocks and caves. These are long-lived and territorial fish: their knowledge of the neighbourhood assists their search for food and shelter.

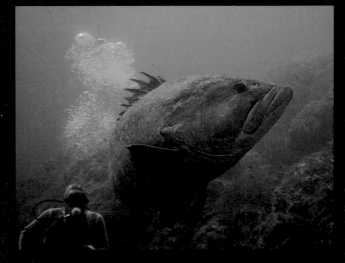

THE AERIAL PREDATORS

The seabirds present in the Mediterranean reflect the distribution of life below the surface, which is concentrated in coastal waters. Offshore birds are scarce. Of these, Cory's shearwater (*Procellaria diomedea*) feeds by plunging into the water, while the storm petrel (*Hydrobates pelagicus*) flits over the surface. Both feed on plankton and small fish.

The coastal seabirds approach the marine food web in many ways. Among the fish-eating species, cormorants and shags search for and pursue their food under water, terns dive in after their prey, while pelicans swim on the surface, sometimes working together to herd the fish.

Gulls will take living fish, but generally they are the scavengers of the sea, swooping down on the water or the shore for anything dying or dead that makes an easy meal. At the opposite extreme, the greater flamingo, *Phoenicopterus ruber*, is a specialist feeder, living on a diet of plankton that it filters from the water of coastal lagoons and mudflats.

Graceful dipper
The common tern or sea swallow (*Sterna hirundo*, below) gracefully quarters the coastal seas searching for small fish. Once they are found, the bird dips briefly down to pluck one from the water.

Pelican patrol
White pelicans (*Pelecanus erythrorhyncus*, right) fly in columns, searching for a shoal of fish. They follow the leading bird down to alight, and swim in a decreasing circle to round up the fish.

Mediterranean speciality
Audouin's gull (*Larus audouinii*, left) is unique to the Mediterranean; but today there are only about 6,000 pairs still in existence.

Europe's smallest seabird
The storm petrel (*Hydrobates pelagicus*, above) is only 15 cm long. It comes on land at night, and its main Mediterranean breeding site is on Malta.

Waiting for a meal
Black-headed gulls (*Larus ridibundus*, right, in winter plumage) are small gulls whose opportunist nature has come to the fore in recent years: they have spread inland, working over rubbish tips for food. A frequent raiding companion is the larger herring gull (*Larus argentatus*) of which a singleton can be seen here.

Coastal shearwater
The manx shearwater (*Puffinus puffinus*, left) feeds on surface plankton in coastal waters. Shearwaters are truly birds of the ocean, sleeping and feeding on the water and coming ashore only in the breeding season. The blending from grey to white plumage on this bird's shoulder shows it belongs to the eastern Mediterranean race.

A sea of seas

The Mediterranean is not a single homogeneous ocean. It is a series of seas, each defined by the land that surrounds it and by the contours of the sea floor. The basic division is between eastern and western Mediterranean, in the shape of a submarine ridge that runs between Sicily and Tunisia.

Each half of the sea is also divided into smaller seas centred on the basins in the sea floor. At the extreme west is the Alboran basin between Spain and Morocco. Between Algeria, France and Sardinia lies the Algerian or Balearic basin; the Ligurian basin lies between Italy and Corsica, while Sardinia, Sicily and Italy enclose the Tyrrhenian.

The eastern Mediterranean contains two of the most famous seas in history: the Adriatic and Aegean. Both are shallow cul-de-sacs of water set between Italy and Yugoslavia, and Greece and Turkey, respectively; the Aegean, whose southern boundary is marked by Crete, is studded with over a thousand islands. To the west, and south of the Adriatic, lies the Ionian basin. Here is the deepest part of the Mediterranean, which plunges to 5,121 metres off the west coast of the Peloponnese. A shallow patch of sea, marked on some maps as the Libyan Sea, between Crete and the Akhdar heights in North Africa, separates the Ionian from the Levantine basin in the east.

Mapping the seabed
The submarine contours of the Mediterranean (right), mapped by a satellite from space. The satellite detects minute changes in gravity that result from the different amounts of rock lying immediately beneath it.

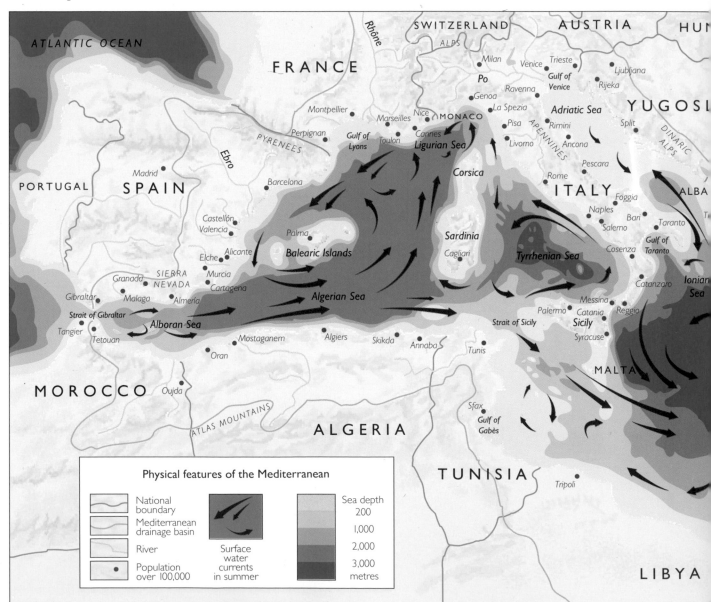

Physical features of the Mediterranean

- National boundary
- Mediterranean drainage basin
- River
- Population over 100,000
- Surface water currents in summer

Sea depth
- 200
- 1,000
- 2,000
- 3,000 metres

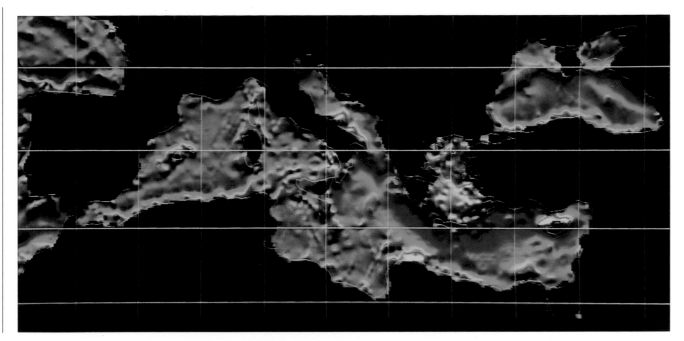

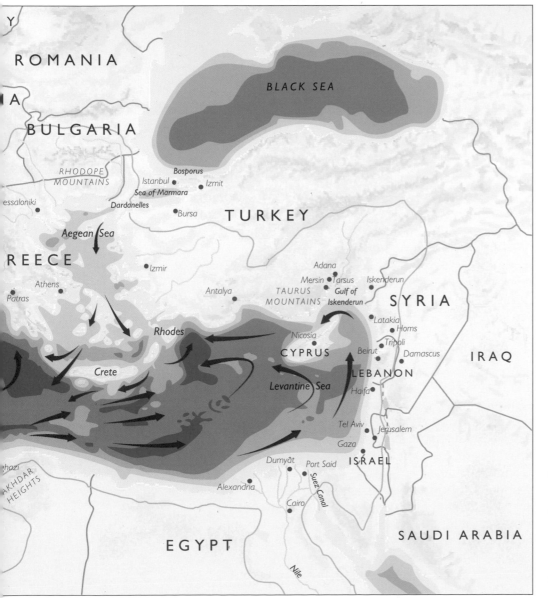

Features of the sea
The map shows the Mediterranean Sea and the various smaller seas within it, as well as its links to the Atlantic Ocean, the Black Sea and the Red Sea.
The main surface current of the Mediterranean flows eastwards along the African coast, with minor branches feeding anti-clockwise currents in other parts of the sea. There is a return current in deeper water, flowing from east to west and out into the Atlantic.
The map also shows the major rivers that flow into the Mediterranean and its drainage area, and names the main towns and cities that line its shores.

The enclosed nature of the Mediterranean, and the way it is split up into separate sub-seas and divided by islands, makes it a physical curiosity. No part of the sea, or the sea as a whole, is large enough to allow water to build up in a large enough body to create a noticeably high or low watermark. The Mediterranean is a virtually tideless sea.

The shaping of the landscape

The Mediterranean today is almost entirely surrounded by mountains. The exception is the 3,000-kilometre-long stretch between the Nile delta and the Atlas mountains on the southeastern coast, which is significantly broken only by the Akhdar highlands in eastern Libya. Between the mountains and the sea is a low-lying coastal strip that is rarely more than 20 or 30 kilometres wide, and sometimes less than a tenth of that. People have traditionally lived, worked, and cultivated the land in between, on the foothills of the mountains or on the higher ranges of the coastal plain.

Land around the Mediterranean can be cultivated only with immense and sustained effort. Indeed, the uniformity of conditions and climate all around the sea's coasts has made the basic patterns of life strikingly similar throughout the region. And, while the Mediterranean's fundamental physical features have deeply influenced human life there, so has human adaptation to these harsh conditions had its effect upon the Mediterranean environment.

Much of what we take for granted about the 'typical' Mediterranean coastal settlement has been shaped by humanity. It is no accident, for instance, nor merely through military prudence, that the typical Mediterranean village is on a hilltop or a mountain slope. For most of recorded history the land below, the strip of flat ground between the hills and the sandy or rocky shore itself, has been a malaria-ridden swamp.

From the mountain to the sea
The traditional settled Mediterranean coastal slope, from barren and inhospitable mountain to rich and fertile seashore plain, still survives in many essentials throughout the region, even on the heavily developed Spanish Costa Blanca (above). Immediately below the bare mountain and behind the villages lie pastures and forest. Below the villages is terraced farmland, *maquis,* and forest grassland. Where the land levels out, the original swamp has been cleared for irrigated farming. On the sea's edge, however, where once pines (and in Spain, palms, imported by the Moors after the 8th century) stood along an empty beach, tourist complexes and industry have covered the shore. And in many places, as people have left the land, the mountain pasture and terraces have reverted to scrub.

To make the plains habitable, the first need was to build drains, so that the water flowed away and offered the mosquitoes that carried the disease no chance to breed. Next, the land had to be irrigated with a flow of fresh water, to keep the mosquitoes at bay and nourish crops.

The rich gardens typical of the lowlands of numerous small Mediterranean islands and communities were probably established by the first human occupants. There are traces of an underground canal network across the Roman Campagna that date back to neolithic times. Other, larger plains were settled in antiquity: in Tunisia and southern Syria, for instance. Some resisted any development at all for hundreds of years: the Mitidja in Algeria was first settled in the late 16th century, but it was only at the end of the 19th century that it was finally made safe and fruitful for humans, with the aid of French engineers. The Pontine marshes around Rome were drained at last on the eve of the Second World War. Most of Greece was plagued by malaria until the late 1940s, when a massive programme financed by the United Nations rid the plains of fever.

But once the coastal plains were habitable, it was also possible to colonize them from without. The defeat of malaria was at the time a magnificent achievement for agriculture; but in later years it was to allow what might be considered a new plague, tourism, to become rampant in the region.

The shrinking forest

The characteristic dry, stony Mediterranean hillside, covered in scrubby *maquis* (a near-impenetrable tangle of low bushes and shrubs) or the even more sparse *garrigue*, is likewise not natural, but the result of human intervention in the landscape. To judge from ancient records, the Mediterranean was once rich in trees. They covered the foothills and lower slopes of the mountains everywhere, from Spain to Algeria, from Greece to Lebanon. In classical times Lebanon's fabled cedar forest was more than 100 kilometres long and on average 1.5 kilometres wide. Today, in many places where those magnificent cedars once stood, bare limestone is all that remains. The forest has been reduced to 14 widely spaced stands of trees.

The shrinking of the cedar forests in Lebanon is in many ways typical of the deforestation that occurred all around the Mediterranean. Like every other country in the region, Lebanon has been invaded and battled over for most of its history. Invaders have typically occupied the plains and fertile lower slopes, and the displaced peoples have literally taken to the hills (the Druze in Lebanon, who fled the Turkish armies in the 12th century, still live there). The amount of available arable land in the eastern Mediterranean is tiny: so refugees have cleared the forests and sown the land in order to survive. And with the people have come their goats, which because of the lack of arable land are far more important in the local economy than elsewhere in the region. Goats, notoriously, graze upon anything, and have given tree shoots no chance to grow and re-establish the former forest.

The same story could be told of countless once green and fertile places around the shores of the sea. And the same essential theme has been repeated constantly throughout the history of the region: the needs of human survival, even at the most basic subsistence level, have ravaged the very land — and, lately, the sea — on which people have depended to stay alive.

The advent of a modern money economy — mainly through tourism or the oil industry — has joined traditional Mediterranean societies to the modern world, and created different criteria of 'survival'. But the environment has paid an horrific price in the process. The rest of this book details the cost of that progress and the chances of saving the Mediterranean as we know it.

The omnivorous goat
A young goatherd tends his flock in Turkey. Goats are vital to traditional economies of the eastern and southern Mediterranean, but no plant can survive their onslaught. Most Mediterranean countries lost their trees to the demands for fuel and building, and the goats have stopped them regenerating.

COUNTRY FILES

MOROCCO
al-Mamlaka al-Maghrebia
Kingdom of Morocco

AREA 458,730 sq km. **MEDITERRANEAN COAST** 500 km.
POPULATION 26,249,000.

Morocco is a constitutional monarchy, with an elected government formed from the Chamber of Representatives; the sovereign retains real political power, however.

THE PEOPLE
Nearly half the Moroccan people speak one of three Berber languages; the remainder speak Arabic. Almost all are of mixed Arab–Berber stock. Over 40% live in cities, of which the largest is Casablanca (pop. 3.5 million); the capital is Rabat (pop. 1 million). The population is expected to reach 40 million by 2000. A low rate of literacy, few media and considerable government control leave little room for expressing or disseminating views that are not officially approved.

THE ECONOMY
LABOUR FORCE 39% in agriculture and fisheries, 20% in services, 17% in industry.
MAJOR EXPORTS Phosphates and derived products, fruit, canned fish, textiles, oil (Morocco refines crude petroleum but has low oil reserves). Tourists (about 2 million annually) are a vital source of foreign currency.
MAJOR IMPORTS Capital goods, fuel, food, iron, steel.

MINERAL RESOURCES Phosphates (Morocco has 75% of the world's reserves), lead, cobalt, manganese, copper.
CHIEF CROPS Cereals, citrus fruits, dates, grapes.
VEHICLES 255,000 commercial, 554,000 cars.

THE ENVIRONMENT
THE PRESENT Most pollution in Morocco comes from factories and plants on the Atlantic coast. The Mediterranean coast remains mostly unspoiled because mountains make it largely inaccessible from the land; there is reason to believe that a few monk seals have found safe breeding grounds here. However, some textile industries do dump waste into the irrigation canal system. Wildlife is abundant, but hunting is common and often indiscriminate. Fishing is crucial to the economy, and tuna are caught both in the Atlantic and in the Mediterranean; Spanish boats fish illegally in Moroccan territorial waters.
THE FUTURE There is little non-governmental activity on behalf of the environment. The result is that potentially damaging government policies go unchallenged, and short term economic interests take first place. Morocco is involved with Mauritania, Algeria, Tunisia and Libya in establishing a Maghreb economic community, which may become active in regional ecological issues.

A coastal enterprise
Small, artisanal boats (below) are still very much a feature of Morocco's Mediterranean fishing fleet.

ALGERIA
al-Jumhuriya al-Jazairiya ad-Dimuqratiya ash-Shabiya
Democratic and Popular Republic of Algeria

AREA 2,381,750 sq km. LENGTH OF COASTLINE 1,200 km.
POPULATION 25,714,000.

The Algerian republic was a one-party state until the 1989 constitution allowed multi-party democracy.

THE PEOPLE
Of Algeria's peoples, 75% are Arab and 25% Berber, although the Berber language is not officially recognized. The Berbers live mainly in the mountains and desert regions, while 49% of all Algerians live in towns. The largest city is the capital, Algiers, with 3 million people. A further 1 million Algerians work in western Europe, 700,000 of them in France.

THE ECONOMY
LABOUR FORCE 30% in agriculture, forestry and fisheries; 30% in industry; 27% in government and services.
MAJOR EXPORTS Petroleum and gas account for 98% of Algeria's earnings from exports.
MAJOR IMPORTS Capital goods, food, consumer goods.
MINERAL RESOURCES Oil (reserves in 1987 totalled 4.8 billion barrels), natural gas, iron, phosphates, lead, zinc, mercury, uranium.
CHIEF CROPS Cereals, grapes, citrus fruit, olives.
VEHICLES 471,000 commercial, 712,000 cars.

THE ENVIRONMENT
THE PRESENT There is very heavy industrial pollution on the eastern Algerian coastline, especially around Annaba and Skikda, and oil pollution is heavy. Algiers discharges all its sewage untreated into the sea. Fishing with dynamite is common. Attempts to reforest the land with eucalyptus trees have only contributed to further desertification. Algeria has four coastal and wetland protected areas.
THE FUTURE The government is developing agriculture and moving industry away from crowded coastal cities, which should at least stabilize the amount of pollution reaching the sea. Algeria is a partner in the nascent Maghreb economic union, which, eventually, may combine economic development with environmental concern. Greenpeace initiatives were well received by local NGOs which, although a new phenomenon in Algeria, are enthusiastic with many highly qualified workers. Media interest in environmental issues is high, and the government reacted positively to the visit by the Greenpeace flagship *Sirius* in 1989.

TUNISIA
Al-Djoumhouria At-Tunisia
Republic of Tunisia

AREA 163,610 sq km. LENGTH OF COASTLINE 1,300 km.
POPULATION 8,094,000.

Tunisia is a democracy; government is led by a Prime Minister; the elected President is head of state.

THE PEOPLE
Tunisia's peoples are Arab (98%) and Berber (1.5%); more than half live in cities, mainly on the coast north of Sfax; 60% of the population live in the coastal areas. The population is growing rapidly at 2.5% per annum.

THE ECONOMY
LABOUR FORCE 35% in agriculture, forestry and fisheries; 22% in manufacturing, mining and construction; 11% in trade, banking and insurance.
MAJOR EXPORTS Petroleum, phosphates and derived products, olive oil, finished textiles, fruit. Tourists are also a vital source of foreign currency.
MAJOR IMPORTS Crude oil, machinery, transport equipment, metals, mineral fuels, fertilizer, chemicals, textiles, food.
MINERAL RESOURCES Phosphates, iron, oil (reserves: 1.7 billion barrels), lead, zinc.
CHIEF CROPS Cereals, dates, olives, fruit, vegetables.
VEHICLES 182,000 commercial, 271,000 cars.

THE ENVIRONMENT
THE PRESENT Pollution from industry is severe in the Gulf of Gabès and in the Tunis area, but most of the Tunisian coast remains clean. An unidentified disease, possibly caused by pollution, has struck red mullet in Tunisian waters. The government has recently closed one phosphate factory and banned sea dumping of phosphate wastes from pipelines.
Pesticides are widely and indiscriminately used, and controls on what types are imported appear to be poorly enforced, as prohibited substances still find their way into the country. Since the mid 1980s large towns have treated their domestic sewage (about 90% in Tunis). Air pollution from motor vehicles and industry remains uncontrolled. Three coastal areas are protected, but the building of dams, ports and hotels in some places has resulted in erosion of the shore. Some reforestation has, however, been successful.
THE FUTURE There are several non-governmental environmental groups, and the government's own Centre for the Environment is now receiving support. Tunisia has no plans for nuclear power, and is experimenting with solar power. However, the population is likely to exceed 10.5 million by the end of the century, and there will be pressure to expand the economy through further industrialization and tourism. Such a programme could well aggravate Tunisia's existing environmental problems, despite current efforts to understand and control them.

COUNTRIES OF THE MAGHREB

Morocco, Algeria and Tunisia – the Mediterranean Maghreb countries – are remarkably unlike one another, for all that they border the Mediterranean in the north and reach into the parched wasteland of the Sahara in the south.

Morocco is a garden compared to its neighbours, well watered and fertile, as the Atlas mountains protect arable land from the desert's heat. The climate is semi-tropical, with humidity on the coast. Much of the Mediterranean coast is steep, rocky and largely inaccessible from inland, and so remains undeveloped.

In contrast, only Algeria's narrow coastal strip is farmed, and arable land takes up less than a twentieth of the country's area. Two chains of the Atlas range cross Algeria and enclose a dry plateau. To the south lies the Sahara, covering four fifths of the country.

The Atlas mountains extend into northern Tunisia. In the plain between them are most of Tunisia's farms – nearly a third of the country is arable – and Tunisia's principal river, the Majarda. The land levels out southwards to an arid plain and a series of salt lakes before merging into the barren lands of the Sahara.

Heat and dust
In parts of Algeria (above) the desert reaches to the sea. The coastal plain is between 75 and 150 kilometres wide, but little of it is fertile. In the north east, the lack of human intervention has preserved some of the Maghreb's most important wetlands. The purple heron (*Ardea purpurea*, right) is one of several species that breeds here; some fly from Europe to winter beyond the southern Sahara.

Ichkeul in danger
This freshwater lake (left) in Tunisia is a winter site for hundreds of thousands of birds. But Ichkeul is now threatened by dams designed to help to counter Tunisia's water shortage.

Green and pleasant in Africa
A view from Morocco of the Spanish enclave of Ceuta, the sea beyond, and nearby Spain (above). Morocco's mountains shelter the coast from the ferociously hot desert in the south and help to increase rainfall, so that the north of the country is well-watered. A fifth of the land is farmed, and the government is increasing the extent of irrigated land from 5,000 to 70,000 square kilometres.

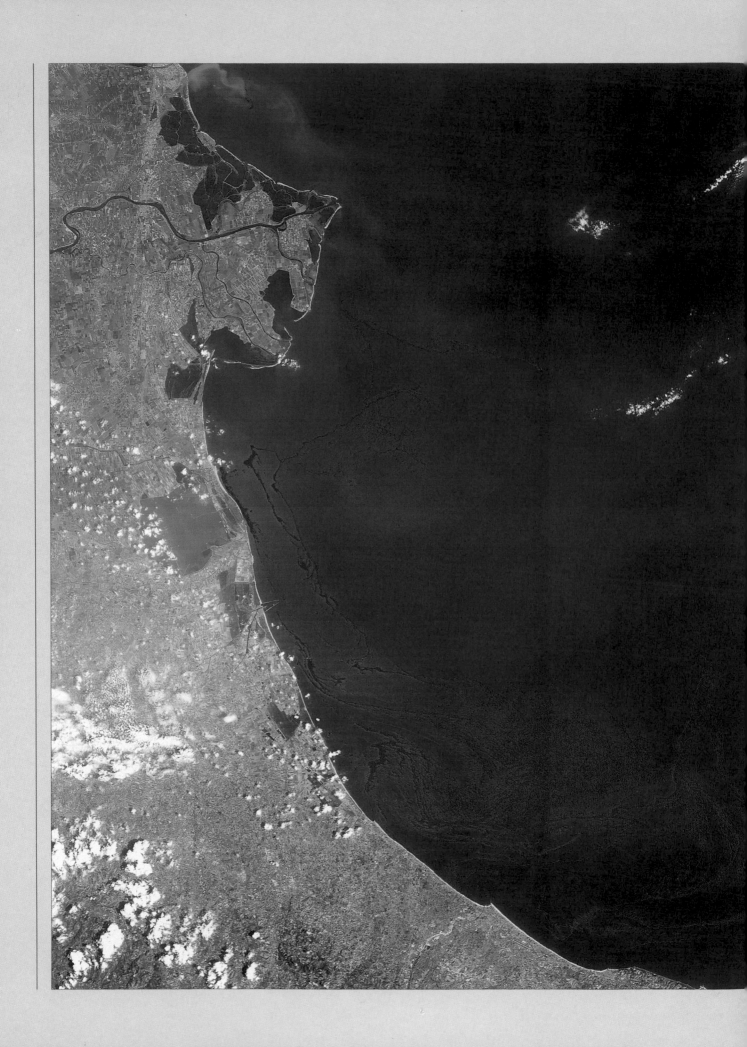

PART

Some 350 million people live in the countries of the Mediterranean basin – 135 million of them around the shores of the sea itself – and they make extraordinary demands on its resources. Waste from towns and cities, farms and factories pours into the Mediterranean; some comes directly from the coast, but most flows relentlessly from the region's four major rivers, the Nile, the Ebro, the Rhône and the Po. Airborne pollution too contaminates the sea; while the consequences of a changing climate brought about by 'greenhouse' gases building up in the atmosphere seem certain to add to the stress already suffered by the Mediterranean environment. A special threat comes from the nuclear industry in the region, and from the persistent presence in the sea of four of the world's nuclear navies. Coupled with the unremitting pressure from the effects of the fishing industry, and the thoughtless tourist developments that are destroying the natural life that draws 100 million people to the region every year, it is not surprising that the Mediterranean is one of the world's most threatened marine ecosystems.

The blooming sea
A colour-enhanced satellite photograph of an algal bloom – an explosion of plant growth as a result of the outpouring of nutrients from industry, agriculture and domestic sewage – in the Adriatic in the summer of 1989. The Adriatic is a microcosm of the crisis facing the Mediterranean: its entire ecosystem is threatened by the human activities on the land around it.

JOURNEY ALONG THE PO

In the middle of a rugged alpine landscape on the borders of France and Italy, the Po starts as a tiny brook between two granite boulders at the edge of the Pian del Re peat bog. In the course of its 675-kilometre journey, the Po collects water from more than 100 tributaries in the Alps and the Apennines before it flows into the Adriatic Sea through a wide delta south of Venice.

The Po is the fourth longest river flowing into the Mediterranean (after the Nile, Ebro and Rhône), and it crosses one of the more intensely populated and industrialized areas of the Mediterranean basin. Some 16 million people live here, releasing into the Po – from their homes, industry and livestock – as much organic waste as would be produced by 119 million. The river touches the four most productive regions in Italy – Piedmont, Lombardy, Emilia Romagna and Veneto – where 50 percent of Italian industry is situated, producing about 25 million tonnes of waste per year. Most of this reaches the Adriatic and ultimately affects the health of the Mediterranean.

In recent years, the appalling pollution of the Adriatic has become increasingly obvious, and the effects on the ecosystem – and on income from tourism – have been devastating. People have finally been forced to realize, after decades of neglecting both river and sea, that something must be done.

In April 1990 the Piedmont regional authorities established the Regional Park of the Po, which covers the third of the river from its source to the boundary with Lombardy. The park management's aim is to regulate human activities and the use of land in the flood plain, in order to protect what remains of the natural life there. A government authority for the drainage basin, recently set up in Parma, may also help to improve the river's sorry plight.

A good deal of money has already been spent on attempting to purify the waters of the Po and the Adriatic, but the level of contamination has gradually worsened. The authorities must now acknowledge that the condition of the river and the sea – and of the whole Mediterranean – cannot be improved by controlling pollution, only by preventing it.

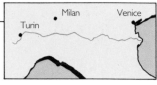

At the source
Mount Monviso towers above Lake Chiaretto (below), whose waters add to melting snow to form the source of the Po.

Alpine beauty
Tumbling down the steep mountainside (below), the clear, fresh waters at the start of the Po bring life to a marvellous variety of alpine flowers (above). Since the upper Po valley lost two thirds of its inhabitants, most of whom moved towards Turin in the 1960s, very little affects the quality of the water in the first 20 kilometres of the river, which are still healthy and clean.

Pilgrimage to the Po
On summer Sundays hundreds of people travel to the source of the Po from all over northern Italy. They use the Pian del Re peat bog as a car park (left and above), destroying rare alpine flora and fauna. At sunset, when the last vehicle is gone, the area will look very much like a dump site as picnic remains, empty bottles and tin cans litter the ground and spoil the water.

CHANGING NATURE

Very few natural wetlands and woods are left in the flood plain of the Po and, in spite of environmentalists' efforts to conserve them, even these vital habitats are still in danger. Several hundred thousand hectares of land have already been turned over to poplar plantations, and farmers continue to demand new areas be cleared or drained for agriculture.

The main responsibility for having changed the nature of the river itself lies with Ministry for Public Works. To stop flooding, the authority has turned the Po into a virtual canal, lining the banks with stone and concrete. Making the river stiff and straight has speeded up its flow, preventing the natural cleansing process, which absorbs nutrients, that usually takes place in the slow-moving water close to the banks.

The authority also grants permits for sand and gravel to be extracted from the river bed. In the early 1980s, between 6 and 7 million cubic metres were taken every year. The Po has been unable to replenish this huge loss and, as a result, the river bed has been lowered by more than 2 metres, as has the level of ground water in the area, thus drying out the land. But worst of all, perhaps, is the effect this industry has on the Adriatic: so little sediment is now taken to the sea by the river that the coast is eroding rapidly.

Controlling the flow
In an attempt to prevent flooding, the Italian river authority has turned the Po into a canal by covering the banks with concrete blocks (above).

Across a cultivated plain
The Po, seen from the Monferrato hills of Piedmont (left), flows across intensively cultivated country. Surrounded by wide willow woods and wetlands until the Second World War, the river has since suffered badly from the demands of agriculture. Now narrow strips of natural woods on the riverside sit among endless rows of poplars and monocultural farmland.

Friends and allies
The gauge of a healthy environment, a damselfly (left) rests on a leaf in a pool left by the river along one of its former beds. Wet woods, marshes and branches of the stream where the water slows down play a vital role in the river's ecology.

A regiment of trees
Rows of hybrid Canadian poplars (above) are one of the most common sights along the Po, in whose catchment area 80 percent of Italian poplar production is concentrated. Greedy for new soil, some poplar growers illegally uproot natural woods in the river's flood plain and even on its islands. The plantation soil is ploughed four times a year and the trees are sprayed with a massive amount of pesticides. No more than 10 species of bird nest in this artificial habitat, while rain washes the chemicals from the soil, adding new compounds to the river's pollution.

AGRICULTURE

The Po flood plain is the most productive land in Italy: as much as a third of the catchment area is given over to intensive forms of agriculture. In order to maintain production, farmers use thousands of tonnes of pesticides, herbicides and artificial fertilizers. When it rains, the chemicals are leached from the soil into the river and its tributaries, down to the Adriatic.

Some toxic chemicals absorbed by the ground produce their dangerous effects long before they reach the waters of the Adriatic: herbicides such as atrazine, simazine and molinate recently contaminated wells of several towns and villages from Casale Monferrato in Piedmont to Rovigo in Veneto, forcing the authorities to fall back on army and fire brigade tankers to supply water to thousands of people.

Farming contributes 6,000 tonnes of phosphorus and 111,000 tonnes of nitrogen to the Adriatic every year, and it is these nutrients that help to create the green and brown algal scum that presently plagues the sea. Eleven million intensively reared cows and pigs contribute to this load. So much waste is produced that the livestock units have a huge problem disposing of it — and most of it ends up in the river. Most farmers devote vast areas of valuable soil to growing crops to feed this enormous number of animals. But, having no animals themselves to enrich the ground, they use large quantities of chemical fertilizers. And both the river and the sea, fertilized and overfed, are the victims of this absurd way of farming.

More is less
Brownish foam from chemical fertilizers, photographed at Casale Monferrato in mid summer (above), illustrates the heavy impact of intensive farming on the Po. So much water is taken for irrigation that, during the hottest months, toxic pollutants become even more concentrated, thus increasing the danger to wildlife (below) and people.

Factory farming
Millions of pigs and cows live in the harsh conditions of intensive animal units (right) throughout the Po catchment area, mostly in Lombardy and Emilia Romagna. In their short lives, they produce three times as much organic pollution as the 16 million people who live in the area. Such is the demand for meat that in some regions 80 percent of arable land is given over to growing food for animals.

Food for the soil
Legally, every pig farmer must keep a certain amount of land to allow for dispersal of slurry (above). Yet some farmers still discharge their tanks directly into the river.

Chemical weapons
Over 7 tonnes of pesticides (right) end up in the river every year. Ground water can be affected too: recently, hundreds of wells became contaminated and had to be closed.

WATER TROUBLES

The hard-working heart of the Italian economy, the Po plain is always thirsty. Of an annual average rainfall of 75 billion cubic metres, human activities in the catchment area consume more than 26 billion, over three quarters of which are taken for agriculture. Since Italian law allows the total exploitation of the river's water, dried up river beds are a common sight all around the basin.

Paradoxically, the risk of sudden catastrophic floods has dramatically increased as humans have tried to regulate the river to suit their needs. In November 1951 a terrible flood, flowing at 12,000 cubic metres per second, caused the embankments to collapse at Occhiobello, near Ferrara, and inundated thousands of kilometres of farmland, killing more than 100 people and thousands of animals. Mountain slopes denuded by tree felling combined with the canalization of rivers to concentrate extraordinary amounts of rain water in a short time and space, triggering off the disaster.

Although deforestation for new alpine ski slopes has come to an end, rain now flows faster than ever from the catchment area to the Po, as housing, industry and roads have made 14,000 square kilometres of ground waterproof. According to Professor Giuliano Cannata of Siena University, a meteorological event like the one of 1951 would now cause the river to flow at such a rate, over 14,000 cubic metres per second, that the embankments would be unable to hold it.

Trout rescue
Flowing through the metropolitan area of Turin, 100 or so kilometres from the source, the Po is a wide, slow river. But in the following 100 kilometres, the quantity of water decreases dramatically, being diverted into three long irrigation canals or pumped out to satisfy the thirst of the cities. In August 1990, river water near Casale Monferrato became so shallow, warm and low in oxygen that fish were asphyxiated, even killed. This sequence of photographs shows anglers Piero Attardo and Mauro Colombano trying to save hundreds of marmor trout from the semi-dry river bed just below the Casale dam. Working at night to avoid exposing the fish to heat, the anglers catch the fish one by one and release them into the fresher waters of the dam's basin.

An everlasting thirst
Modern irrigation systems (left) help farmers in the Po valley to produce some of the world's highest yields per hectare. Water taken from the Po for farming has rocketed to 18 billion cubic metres a year, about 36 percent of all water consumption in Italy.

Not a drop to drink
In Piedmont in summer, when long periods of drought increase farmers' demand for water, great stretches of the river dry up. Near Revello, natural drainage helps to empty the Po of its last drop. The river bed is so dry (below) that a gypsy family have been able to camp here. But their water must be brought in jerry cans from the nearby village.

Rock bottom
The rocky river bed is exposed (above) less than a kilometre from the Casale dam. The little water in the river was released after the keeper of the dam heard that the fish were dying.

POLLUTION

There was a time when the waters of the Po were regarded as almost magical. Doctors sent patients to the river to heal wounds and cure skin ailments. Fishermen and ferrymen used to drink the water directly; swimmers crowded the sandy banks. The river was a favourite resort until the late 1960s when the first signs of serious pollution began to show.

Everything has grown larger since then: the cities and industrial plants are bigger; the livestock units more intensive, and there is the endless monotony of monocrop agriculture. Today, the scale of most human activities in the plain increases pollution dramatically: 65 tonnes of mercury, 243 tonnes of arsenic, 485 of lead and other heavy metals, together with persistent synthetic compounds, enter the Po every year. Urban sewage reaches the river, too: bathing is now illegal in these waters because the risk of disease is so high.

The Italian Ministry of the Environment recently announced a 5,000 billion lire scheme to control pollution in the catchment area. The proposal includes the construction of large sewage plants to reduce the amounts of bacteria and nutrients entering the river — even though a similar plant for the Garda Lake has resulted in a massive increase in nutrient pollution. Furthermore, an experiment on the Trebbia (which flows into the Po) had shown that wetlands are extraordinarily effective in filtering outflows from small sewage plants, and it would cost far less to create new wetlands to do this than to build huge treatment plants. All of which seems to have been ignored.

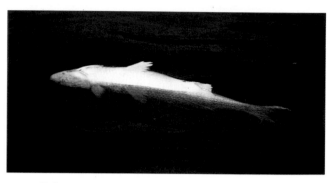

Polluters unknown
A foamy liquid released illegally into the sewers by industrial pirates emerges at the outfall in the river at Turin (below).

Death of a fish
Toxic metals and synthetic chemicals, lack of oxygen and too many nutrients make life hard for the fish of the Po.

Pulito é (Clean is...)
An advertising slogan ironically points out urban waste floating in the Po at Turin (above). Although one of the most effective water treatment plants in Italy has been operating in the city since 1984, signs of pollution still show up along the river.

Toxic cocktail
A lethal mixture of heavy metals and toxic chemicals is discharged from a pesticides factory into the river (above).

Roads to ruin
Technological waste like this pile of wrecked cars (left) retains hazardous substances (lead, mercury, oils, acids, and even the ozone-destroying CFCs in air-conditioning units) until the metal has corroded and leakage begins. Encouraged by a powerful automobile industry, Italians tend to change their cars often.

INTO THE SEA

The Adriatic is a small, shallow sea and no more than 200 kilometres wide. It makes up just 5 percent of the total surface of the Mediterranean, but it receives 33 percent of Mediterranean fresh waters, mostly from the Po. And the river is delivering steadily higher quantities of pollutants to the sea.

Eutrophication or overfertilization is the most visible danger facing the Adriatic – it also has the greatest impact. Troubles began in 1975 with an enormous algal bloom of tens of millions of cells per litre, whose death and subsequent decay used up the oxygen in the water and killed many thousands of fish, molluscs and crustaceans living on the seabed. Since then, algal blooms have happened nearly every summer.

In both 1988 and 1989 a brown slurry on the sea's surface kept millions of tourists away from the beaches of Emilia Romagna, damaging a 5,000 billion lire business that gave employment to 200,000 people.

Trouble comes to the Adriatic, too, from the petrochemical industry concentrated in areas such as Ravenna and in Porto Marghera, near Venice, which releases conspicuous amounts of toxic waste into the Venice Lagoon.

Sceptical about the government's plans for saving the Adriatic, the tourist industry has built large amusement centres equipped with huge swimming pools to serve as substitutes for the sea. This may be good business, but, to many, it is a sign of defeat.

Shaving the sea
A specially equipped dredger removes algae from a lagoon in the Po delta. These machines damage life on the sea bottom.

Industrial seascape
Tanks, pipes and metal frames rise behind a tanker's berth in an oil refinery near Ravenna – a stronghold of the oil industry.

Substitute for a dying sea
'Aquafun' centres like this one near Riccione (left) are becoming a common sight along the Adriatic riviera.

Wooden skeletons
Tree stumps hurled into the Po by poplar growers end up hundreds of kilometres away on the shores of the delta (below).

Too close for comfort?
Tourists on the Adriatic riviera (above) add to the tonnes of sewage brought daily into the sea by the river Po. With an average density of 45 hotels per kilometre of coast, the seaside resorts of Emilia Romagna are the most intensive tourist centres in the country.

POLLUTION
WAVES OF SICKNESS

I
N SEPTEMBER 1983 scientists in the Gulf of Trieste watched, horrified, as in little more than a week over 90 percent of the fish, brittle-stars, shellfish and other invertebrates that live on the seabed died through lack of oxygen. In the Saronikos Gulf off Athens a zone of death grows larger every year: during the summer, marine life is forced to retreat to the fringes of the gulf as the oxygen disappears. Similar events have been documented in the Turkish Sea of Marmara. Others may well go unnoticed elsewhere.

These death zones on the seabed are but one symptom of the sickness that is afflicting the Mediterranean. Paradoxically, they often go hand in hand with unnatural, luxuriant plant growth in the waters above. In some cases the sea becomes a thick soup of microscopic algae, which eventually creates a slimy brown scum on the water that washes up on the shore. In the Adriatic some blooms have reached a density of 100 million cells per litre of water. In the Venice Lagoon algal growth has reached a million tonnes a year, with up to 50 kilograms of algae produced per square metre. One third of Lake Tunis, in Tunisia, once a coastal lagoon rich in wildlife, is now choked with drifts of green ribbon-like seaweed up to a metre deep.

Signs of the Mediterranean's malaise can be seen throughout the length and breadth of the sea. Most shocking is the death of thousands of striped dolphins in the western Mediterranean, whose bodies began to be washed up on the shore in July 1990. Massive breeding failures have been reported for bonito tuna and mackerel in the Turkish Sea of Marmara, for grey mullet in Abu Qîr Bay, east of Alexandria, and for fish in the Gulf of Naples, Cagliari and the Venice Lagoon, while the Bay of Muggia at Trieste has become a desert. In the late 1980s many red mullet caught in the water off Sfax and Sousse in Tunisia were found to be suffering from a previously unknown disease while, further west, some species that have been a staple food in the region for centuries, including tuna and pilchard, contain so much mercury that, if the law were to be enforced, they could not be sold.

The 40 or so years that have seen these afflictions beset the marine life of the Mediterranean have also seen a remarkable change in the lives of the people around its shores. Many people have moved from rural areas to the cities, and the population has increased from 220 million to 360 million, while the 132 million living in the coastal regions play host to 100 million

Death in the gulf
A rich and diverse community of animals normally thrives in the sediment of the Gulf of Trieste, in the northern Adriatic (below left). But in early September 1983, over an area of several hundred square kilometres, the oxygen virtually disappeared from the bottom waters and within days a coating of mucus had smothered much of the life on the seabed (below). Sewage discharges into the sea, which become particularly heavy during the tourist season, are suspected to be the cause of this catastrophe. Although there had been reports of similar events in the gulf in previous years, this was the first time the exact sequence of events had been documented.

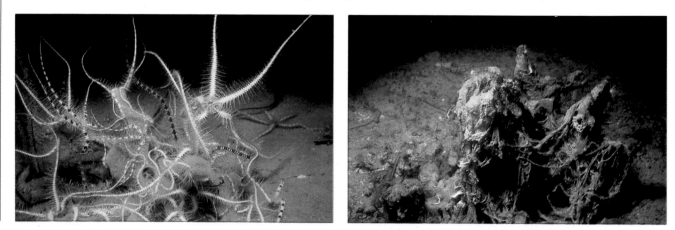

visitors in the summer months. There have been huge increases in energy consumption, the extraction of raw materials and their transportation across the sea and beyond, and in manufacturing and consumption.

There is now strong evidence that the unmistakable signs of deterioration in the health of the sea and the changes that people have experienced around its shores are linked by a single thread – a massive increase in pollution, from homes, from industry and from intensive farming.

FROM PARADISE TO CESSPOOL

One of the direct consequences of the expansion of the cities was the creation of an urban sewage network. As a result, raw sewage from between 70 and 85 percent of the population is discharged straight into the Mediterranean, along with animal and plant waste from food processing and other similar industries. The coastal waters and shallow bays of the sea tend to retain this material, and here bacteria feed on it and break it down, using up life-giving oxygen as they do so. In the worst cases, so much sewage is discharged into the sea that the bacteria remove all of the oxygen from the water, killing life here and on the seabed.

Even when marine organisms are not killed outright, the effluent has an effect. Any remaining organic material sinks to the bottom of the sea, where opportunist creatures that thrive in the disintegrating mass displace the usual bottom-dwelling species. The stress caused by the shortage of oxygen is believed to have contributed to the increased incidence of fin rot in fish, and a similar deterioration in the shells and gills of crustaceans. There may well be many other consequences too, if human experience is anything to go by. Among known effects are sickness and diarrhoea, dermatitis, conjunctivitis, and, at worse, cholera and typhoid.

The *mare sporco*
A diver struggles through a blanket of microscopic algae held together by their gelatinous secretions. This form of algal bloom, for which the Adriatic has become notorious, is graphically described by its Italian name of *mare sporco* – 'dirty sea'. The algae sink to the bottom where they die and rot, removing the oxygen from the water. Both the scale and the frequency of algal blooms appear to be increasing, almost certainly as a result of the additional nutrients that now enter the Adriatic in sewage discharges and the effluent from intensive livestock units, from agricultural fertilizers washed down to the sea, and as by-products from the burning of fossil fuels.

A stain around the sea

This outpouring of effluent has created a stain around the rim of the Mediterranean. The Alexandrian waterfront, for example, once offered escape from the hot, dusty alleys of the city. But today it is choked with the stinking mass of untreated sewage and effluent from abattoirs, canneries, tanneries and dairies, along with other industrial and domestic waste. Further to the east, in Turkey's Sea of Marmara, bays are filling in with effluent and soil eroded from the surrounding land. Across the Aegean the contamination stretches 300 kilometres down the west coast from Thessaloniki to Cape Sounîon, where it turns north to the Saronikos Gulf, the unfortunate recipient of waste from municipal Athens. Here and around the islands this effluent is matched annually by the 50,000 tonnes of waste from olive oil production that is discharged into the water.

The northern Adriatic is shallow and enclosed. Into this vulnerable area the Po valley alone discharges the effluent from 16 million people and the slurry from intensive livestock units equivalent to a further 62 million people. This in turn is virtually doubled by waste from other agriculture and the food-processing industry. The gulfs of Venice and Trieste fare worst, but huge problems extend far to the south.

The longest stretch of fouled coastline runs at least 1,000 kilometres from the Arno in northwest Italy, along the French coast to the Rhône and on to the Ebro in Spain. In this area the coastal discharges alone are responsible for removing 336 tonnes of oxygen from every kilometre of water every year. Effluents entering from the rivers remove around 1 million tonnes of oxygen from the water every year, along with a further 370,000 tonnes from the coastal waters of the Tyrrhenian Sea.

Over-fertility

The deoxygenation of the water is only half the story. The micro-organisms that remove the oxygen also break down the organic matter into inorganic material, two groups of which, nitrogen and phosphorus compounds, are major fertilizers or nutrients. Enormous amounts of nitrogen also enter the

Raw sewage
The rapid growth of coastal towns and cities in the Mediterranean, coupled with a shortage of funds for proper urban development, means that streams have been pressed into service as open sewers (below), and that between 70 and 85 percent of sewage remains untreated when it is disgorged into the sea (above).

sea when agricultural fertilizers are leached from the soil. In natural circumstances, the surface waters around the coast of the Mediterranean carry only low levels of nutrients, and adding such huge amounts has drastic effects on marine life – the most visible of which are the algal blooms now choking the inshore waters in so many parts of the sea. The northern Adriatic has been most severely affected, but blooms have also been reported in Izmir Bay, Turkey, in Elefsis Bay in Greece, around Valencia in Spain and in the Tunis Lagoon. When the blooms die they fall to the seabed and rot and, like the sewage sludge, use up masses of oxygen in the process. And as the size and frequency of blooms appear to be increasing, so too do the amounts of nutrients entering the sea.

In the 1970s it was thought that some 800,000 tonnes of nitrogen compounds were swept into the sea from coastal discharges and rivers each year. This dwarfed natural inputs of around 200,000 tonnes. The artificial inputs of phosphorus were put at 320,000 tonnes, eight times the natural level. No subsequent overall calculations have been made, but fertilizer use alone increased by between 50 and 100 percent during the 11 years up to 1981, and today's figures must be larger still. In Greece as much as 650,000 tonnes of nitrogen fertilizer (over a quarter of that applied) now finds its way into the sea. There is no reason to think that Greece is a special case; the situation could be just as bad in other Mediterranean countries.

In addition, huge amounts of nitrogen compounds enter the sea from the atmosphere as a result of burning fossil fuels – gas, coal and oil. No figures are available for the Mediterranean, but in the North Sea and in Chesapeake Bay in the United States it is thought that atmospheric deposition of nitrogen increases marine pollution by 30 percent.

Sights of the Mediterranean
The masses of the green seaweed *Ulva* choking the Venice Lagoon (above) and the algal scum on the beach and in the sea at Cesenatico (below) do nothing for the reputation or income of these and similar coastal resorts.

The infertile Nile
Since the building of the Aswan dam, which holds back fertile silt that used to be deposited annually in the Nile flood plain, agriculture in the Nile valley depends on artificial fertilizers and other chemicals (right).

Mining growth
Phosphate, a nutrient essential for plant growth, is extracted in Tunisia (below). But factory discharges, still rich in phosphate, have stimulated abnormal growth of algae in adjacent coastal waters.

A bleak diagnosis

Present initiatives to cure the Mediterranean's nutrient pollution fall far short of the mark. No co-ordinated action is planned to limit the use of fertilizer or reduce the amount of nitrogen entering the atmosphere. It is intended that by 1995 all cities with populations over 100,000 will stop discharging raw sewage into the sea. But most sewage treatment plants will break down only organic material. The discharges will still contain nitrogen and phosphorus, which will continue to fuel the growth of algae – and still result in the removal of oxygen from the water.

Better methods of breaking down sewage are now being tested, ones that more closely mimic natural processes. Sewage could also be treated as a resource, and the nutrients recovered for use as fertilizer. But this is not yet practical, because sewage is contaminated by toxic waste – containing heavy metals and synthetic chemicals – from both industrial and domestic sources.

A METALLIC TAINT

We have known for many years that heavy metals can be extremely toxic, but believed that our activities discharged insignificant amounts into the environment compared to natural geological processes. Yet, in the 1970s, research in the Mediterranean revealed that human inputs — discharges from sewers as well as industrial discharges directly into the rivers and the sea — formed the major part in all of the four metals studied: lead, chromium, zinc and mercury. The input of lead had increased from its natural level of around 1,000 tonnes per year to 4,800 tonnes per year; chromium had been boosted from 400 to 2,800 tonnes per year, and zinc from 4,000 to 25,000 tonnes, with the greatest amount of pollution going into the northwest Mediterranean, the Adriatic and the Tyrrhenian Sea.

Mercury — by far the most toxic of the metals in the survey — provides a shocking example. The research suggested that about 30 tonnes of mercury entered the Mediterranean naturally, but 100 tonnes a year came from a wide range of other sources, including the manufacture of chlorine, of polyvinyl chloride (PVC) and of many other substances, as well as from metal production. Mercury was even used as a pesticide. Furthermore the pollution was concentrated in two regions of the sea: the northwest Mediterranean and the Adriatic. Later research has revealed that fish in these areas carry unusually high levels of mercury. Pilchards and tuna resident in the northwest Mediterranean on average contain five times more mercury than those at the western end. As a result local people who eat the fish have accumulated levels of mercury that may prove toxic.

Many other metals are discharged into the sea from mining and industry. The impact they have ranges from gradual changes in plankton species, to lethal effects on the eggs, immature and adult forms of shellfish and fish, and

Poisoning the food chain
Marine plants (on the far left of the diagram) grow using dissolved minerals and energy from the sun. Herbivores (in the second box) feed on the plants and themselves fall prey to other animals (third and fourth boxes). The top link in this food chain comprises turtles, mammals and birds (right-hand box). But as this material passes up the food chain (blue arrows), less and less is directly used as food. The rest is converted back into minerals, partly by scavengers (bottom) and partly by the continuous process of excretion throughout the chain. Pollutants such as heavy metals and some synthetic chemicals are readily absorbed with food, but they are not easily excreted, and even organisms low in the chain can be affected by them. The higher the position in the food chain and the longer-lived the individual creature, the more pollution it accumulates (red arrows). Top predators can gather levels of pollutants millions of times greater than those in the water. These may kill them directly, or reduce their ability to cope with disease.

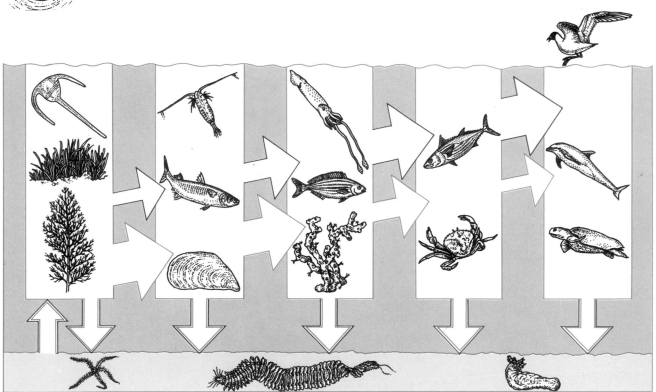

OIL AND TROUBLED WATERS

Every year the waters of the Mediterranean suffer about 635,000 tonnes of oil pollution – roughly one fifth of the global total – making the Mediterranean one of the most oil-polluted seas in the world.

The scale of the problem first became apparent in the 1960s. Ships discharged their oily wastes and bilge slops straight into the sea, while oil tankers washed and ballasted their tanks with sea water, which they then emptied into the Mediterranean. Off southern Italy, near the main shipping lane, oil pollution reached levels of 500 litres per square kilometre. Many beaches throughout the region were spoiled by oil. Fish and shellfish became tainted with oil and were unfit for sale. In badly contaminated areas, marine creatures – including spiny lobsters in Tunisia, tuna and mackerel in the Sea of Marmara, and other species in Italian waters around Naples, Cagliari and Venice – were failing to breed successfully. Trieste's Bay of Muggia was devastated by continual pollution from the local petrochemical industry.

An annex to the International Convention for the Prevention of Pollution from Ships (MARPOL) is supposed to reduce oil discharges at sea significantly. But only nine Mediterranean countries have signed it. There are reception facilities for oily waste for only half of the oil trade; and there are simply not enough surveillance ships or aircraft to monitor the pollution of the sea and therefore bring those responsible to court. As a result, around 330,000 tonnes of oil are still dumped at sea by ships each year. As for oil spills, while there are plans for dealing with emergencies, most countries lack the equipment to carry them out.

On the positive side, the Hellenic Marine Environment Protection Association provides good information to shipowners and seamen in order to prevent pollution from ships. And there are signs that the authorities are becoming more committed to stopping oil pollution: in 1990, for example, the Norwegian owners of a tanker were fined $1 million for discharging oil at sea. But if oil pollution really is to be solved, firm action must become the rule rather than the exception.

Sources old and new

The extraction of gas and oil from the Mediterranean is a growing industry, with 116 platforms now in the sea – in Italy, Tunisia, Libya, Greece, Turkey and Egypt.

Offshore oil production in other seas has been shown to be a significant source of pollution: a well delivering 1,000 tonnes of oil a day spills about 100 kilograms in that time; oil-contaminated water and oil-based drilling muds are also discharged or dumped into the sea, killing life on the bottom. As the Mediterranean offshore industry expands, it must do everything it can to avoid creating these problems.

A huge amount of the oil in the sea actually comes from land, in industrial and municipal waste. Estimates suggest that this could be as much as 305,000 tonnes a year – similar to that from shipping. Oil products are simply dumped in landfills or are discharged into the sewers or rivers; this is disturbing, not only because of the damage it does to rivers and sewage plants (where they exist), but because lubricating oils contain heavy metal and synthetic chemical additives, making them far more dangerous than crude oil.

Oil comes ashore
An oil tanker (left) pumps its cargo ashore at Bizerte, Tunisia. Many tankers, having delivered their load, wash out their tanks and dump the oily waste at sea. Tankers also create pollution when, before taking on a new load, they dump the oil-contaminated seawater that was taken into their tanks as ballast. In many Mediterranean ports there are either no facilities for receiving oily waste, or the facilities that do exist are seriously inadequate. Tanker accidents are another source of pollution. As a result, many otherwise idyllic Mediterranean coastlines, such as this beach in Cyprus (right), are grossly polluted with oil.

The legally binding Barcelona Convention protocol for controlling pollution from land-based sources (see page 112) commits Mediterranean states to prevent lubricating oils reaching the sea, but this comes into effect only in 1995. Until then, prevention will depend on inadequate national legislation.

But any legislation, even if it is strictly enforced, and whether it is national or international, tackles only the symptoms of the disease. The one certain way of significantly reducing oil pollution will be to reduce substantially the amount of oil produced, transported and consumed – by increasing energy efficiency and the use of alternative sources of energy.

Grim icon
Oil kills birds by fouling their plumage and by poisoning them as they are preening (above). Oil slicks smother life on the shore and seep into the sediment where they can be damaging long after visible signs have gone. Oil even has an effect far out to sea because part of it diffuses into the water, harming marine life ranging from plankton to fish.

An unrefined act
An oil refinery (left) on the Etang de Berre, a coastal lagoon adjacent to the mouth of the Rhône. Refineries often discharge waste products into the water and air during normal operations, resulting in the chronic pollution of their surroundings.

A red stain
The bed of the Rio Tinto in southern Spain is stained red by copper, iron and other metals, an effect exacerbated by mining activities. These, along with other sources further downstream, add to the river's burden which, by the time it enters the Gulf of Cadiz, is believed each year to include some 158,000 tonnes of iron, 11,000 tonnes of copper, 52,000 tonnes of zinc and 8,000 tonnes of manganese. Some of this is deposited in the Gulf of Cadiz or enters the Atlantic; the remainder is carried by surface currents through the Strait of Gibraltar to become another of the many sources of pollution in the Mediterranean.

breeding failures or death of seabirds. Local surveys of cadmium, regarded as second only to mercury in its toxicity, show that significant pollution occurs in the waters and sediments off Cartagena and Valencia in Spain, and in the discharges of the river Po to the Adriatic; the Rhône alone is estimated to discharge 70–160 tonnes of cadmium into the sea every year. In Spain, the silver, lead and zinc mining operations at Portman, 100 kilometres south of Alicante, dumped 7,000 tonnes of mine tailings into the sea every day for nearly 30 years. The discharge has now stopped (see page 132), but the contamination remains.

The problems of the northern Mediterranean are spreading south and east as the race to industrialize speeds up. Sediments in the upper Saronikos Gulf in Greece have between 8 and 200 times the natural levels of antimony, arsenic, chromium, mercury, silver and zinc around pipes discharging sewage from Athens, while sediments from the Turkish Bay of Izmir show even higher levels of zinc, copper, lead, cadmium and mercury. Phosphate mining in Tunisia certainly causes pollution; while for many other mining industries, such as the chrome mines in Albania (the third largest in the world), there simply is not enough information to assess the impact on the environment.

Problems arise too from dumping dredging spoil – sludge dredged from shipping channels in harbours and rivers that has become contaminated over many years by industrial pollution. Dredging spoil has been used for land reclamation but, in some areas of the northern Adriatic for example, the level of contamination is so high that it exceeds EC safety standards for metals in soil. Yet still the sludge is dumped at sea. As it sinks to the bottom, some of

Second time around
Rivers, estuaries and harbours such as Valletta in Malta (above) need frequent dredging to keep shipping channels open. But if the dredging spoil is dumped at sea this can release large amounts of contaminants that have accumulated in the sediment – with severe consequences for marine life.

the pollutants dissolve in the water. The rest of the spoil smothers the seabed, killing the creatures that live there. When worms and other life on the bottom have become re-established, they constantly turn over the sludge, keeping the metals in the surface layer, where they are absorbed by marine organisms and passed on up through the food web.

SYNTHETIC DEATH

Another major threat to the Mediterranean comes from the multitude of chemicals used to create a vast range of household and industrial products, including plastics, plasticizers, fabrics, packaging materials, pesticides, aerosols, refrigeration fluids, paints, flame retardants and solvents such as dry cleaning fluids. As a result of these industries tens of thousands of unnatural compounds contaminate the sea.

One important and alarming group of these artificial substances is the halogenated hydrocarbons (HHCs), the result of combining hydrocarbons with chlorine, fluorine, bromine or iodine. As yet scientists have been able to identify completely only some 10 percent of the HHCs that are now found in marine life. One of the known groups, the polychlorinated biphenyls (PCBs), best illustrates the problems associated with HHCs.

PCBs were first synthesized in the 1930s, and their apparent inertness led to their use in fluids to cool electrical transformers (because they did not break down when heated), and as hydraulic fluids in mining equipment (no risk of explosions), and in a host of other applications. But in the 1960s it was discovered that they are extremely destructive in living matter. They cannot easily be broken down or excreted and they are passed on through the food web to accumulate in the tissues of the predators at the end of a chain. Concentrations of PCBs in plankton, invertebrates and fish have been found to lie anywhere between 10,000 and 1 million times those in water, while birds and mammals contain levels perhaps a hundred times greater still.

The visible evidence
Dead fish floating in a French marina. Deaths on this scale, sometimes caused by pollution, seem set to continue unless we adopt precautionary principles in our attitude to the environment – and permit only those activities that have been proved to be harmless.

No smoke without fire
Factories on the Nile throw up black clouds from their furnaces. Conditions like this are found dotted throughout the southern and eastern Mediterranean, and controls on emissions are often lax. But such is the level of industrial production in the countries of the north west that they are responsible for the largest amounts of pollution.

Waste from paper
This pulp and paper factory in Spain, like many others, still uses chlorine-based processes to bleach wood pulp. This results in the production of chlorinated waste, which is drained into the sea. The waste contains dioxins, a group of chemicals that includes the most toxic substances known – a weekly dose of just a few millionths of a millionth of a gram is thought to be unsafe for humans, and even this may be an overestimate. The only responsible action is to eliminate the production of dioxins, which in the case of paper making can be done by switching to manufacturing processes that do not involve chlorine.
This book demonstrates that paper made using these newer methods is of high quality and need not be prohibitively expensive.

PCBs at concentrations as low as 50 parts per trillion inhibit the growth of phytoplankton, while fish may die when levels of PCBs in their body tissue are as low as 0.5 parts per million (ppm). Scientists believe that levels of 10 ppm can put mammals at risk, and that this amount could be accumulated though the food web from a concentration in water of only one part per trillion. Experiments have shown that seals fed on fish that contain levels of PCBs of around 0.2 ppm are only half as fertile as those fed on less-contaminated fish. The same experiments suggested that these levels of PCBs affected the seals' immune system, and PCBs have been suspected of suppressing the ability to fight disease in a whole range of other mammals and birds. In fact, no experiment has ever managed to show that any level of PCBs, in either plants or animals, is safe.

Immense quantities of PCBs enter the northwest Mediterranean and the Adriatic. In the late 1980s over half a tonne of PCBs were being discharged into the Rhône each day, and their concentration in the waters off the river mouth reach up to 400 parts per trillion. The result is that levels of PCBs in fish in these two regions reach one, two or even eight ppm, whereas some countries apply a safety standard for human consumption of 1-5 ppm. Mediterranean dolphins have been found to contain up to 450 ppm of PCBs in their liver and blubber — well above the level at which harmful effects are known to occur in other marine mammals. As a result, scientists and environmentalists are extremely concerned that PCB and other pollution may have exacerbated the viral epidemic that is believed to have killed thousands of dolphins in the western Mediterranean since summer 1990 (see page 128).

PCB concentrations are highest in northern waters, but significant amounts have been measured throughout the sea. Even in the least contaminated waters off the Levant and Egypt, fish carry levels of PCBs still one tenth of those in the most polluted areas. But the effects of synthetic chemicals do not necessarily follow a simple gradient from north west to south east. In the east, as elsewhere, there are now huge problems posed by toxic synthetic chemicals that are deliberately dispersed in the environment – the pesticides.

Killing by design

In 1987 it was estimated that more than 400 tonnes of DDT, lindane and other HHC pesticides enter the Mediterranean each year. The northwestern states certainly contribute to this, but they are not the sole source. Greece, for example, used 14,000 tonnes of pesticides in 1989; in Morocco 7,000 tonnes were used in a typical year; and in the 1980s Egypt sprayed, on average, 15,000 tonnes of pesticides each year, 70 percent of them on the cotton crop destined for sale abroad. The way Egypt has suffered from pesticides is typical of many other countries.

By the end of the 1970s, in a period of about 25 years, Egyptian farmers had released at least 110,000 tonnes of HHC pesticides into the environment. The chemicals persist for years: even now, along the Egyptian coast, the water, sediments and marine life remain badly contaminated. In Abu Qîr Bay and Lake Idku to the east of Alexandria, pollution from endrin, lindane and DDT, along with discharges from industry and sewage, is thought to have contributed to the decline of grey mullet in what was a major breeding area.

As the pests became resistant to HHC pesticides, organophosphorus compounds (developed from military nerve gases) were used instead. Leptophos, introduced in the late 1960s, was found to cause nervous disorders in mammals, including people, and was then banned; but it persisted in the water of the Nile long afterwards. Leptophos was replaced by other organophosphorus pesticides thought to be less persistent. But this may not be enough to prevent them damaging the environment: it is now known that pesticides reach the oceans far more rapidly than was once thought – via the atmosphere – possibly before the chemicals in them have broken down.

The damage caused by synthetic compounds and heavy metals would be bad enough if each acted in isolation, but they may also work together to create even greater harm. It is impossible to monitor the effects of these thousands of compounds, either separately or synergistically, on the thousands of marine species in an ecosystem of whose mechanics we have but the slightest idea. We have failed to monitor effectively even the few regulated substances. It is increasingly clear that if we are to protect the Mediterranean we must prevent its contamination in the first place.

Unnatural fragility
The effects on wildlife of pesticides such as DDT have been known for 30 years. DDT persists in the environment, from where it is absorbed into the living food web. Among other effects, DDT causes birds to lay eggs with abnormally thin shells that can be crushed during incubation (above).
Yet DDT was widely used by Mediterranean countries until only recently; and it is doubtful that governments will act faster over other pesticide problems.

Human vulnerability
People working with pesticides often take few precautions, putting themselves and others at risk. Protective clothing is not worn, fumes are inhaled, sprays are allowed to drift over homes, and remnants may be discarded carelessly. These problems will be overcome only by eliminating pesticides; at the very least, their use should be reduced to the minimum.

URBAN WASTE

Plastic floating in the sea, beaches covered with rubbish, dump sites beside the roads, along the river banks and on the clifftops, refuse burning in the open air – this picture can be seen throughout the Mediterranean region. The unsuitable use, storage and transport of all types of waste, including toxic and dangerous materials, are growing problems all around the Mediterranean. Toxic industrial waste is often stored in municipal dumps along with household refuse, which itself contains hazardous substances. Rain flushes the toxins into the soil, contaminating the earth and ground water. From there they find their way into the rivers and eventually into the sea.

Together with the discharge from boats, coastal dumps are the principal source of plastic in the sea; they cause serious problems in the Mediterranean and can be lethal to marine life. Some 42 species of seabirds, including cormorants, lapwings and seagulls, are known to ingest pieces of plastic that they mistake for food, and these can then be fed to their chicks. Turtles frequently mistake plastic for jellyfish, a key element in their diet. Even when the plastic itself is not poisonous, it can cause the death of the animal by obstructing its digestive system.

Plastics can kill in other ways, too: birds such as pelicans, which swim under water, die of hunger when their beaks become blocked or bound with plastic material; other birds are strangled by plastic can holders; turtles can suffocate in plastic sheeting; and seals die a slow death when they become wrapped in the remains of packaging that tightens around them as they grow. The severity of this form of marine pollution should not be underestimated: 30 percent of Mediterranean fish examined have been found to have plastic debris in their intestines.

No solution in incineration

In some regions, the scale of the rubbish problem has focused attention on the potential for recycling and for reducing the amount of waste material produced. But here too there are problems.

Some have regarded the incineration of rubbish as a means of recycling and have promoted it as an 'energy recovery system', which uses the heat from the incinerator to generate electricity. In reality, the forms of rubbish incineration used have caused considerable pollution through the release of gases and ash, and have produced energy in a very inefficient way. For example in Turkey, the city of Izmir has an effective programme of recycling and composting much of its urban waste, but the residue is burned, either at the dump site or in incineration plants, emitting highly toxic contaminants into the atmosphere.

Incineration serves only to change the nature of the pollution – shifting it from the land to the air. In addition, incineration not only fails to eliminate the problem of dump sites, it actually aggravates the problem by converting the heterogeneous mixture of materials that usually makes up garbage into large quantities of toxic ash that still have to be disposed of.

Recycling, together with reductions in the amount of waste material produced in the first place, forms

the only real solution to the problem of urban waste. Recycling can help significantly to conserve natural resources and to protect wildlife and natural habitats.

Replacing virgin materials with recycled materials reduces contamination of the environment and also saves energy in the manufacture of such products as paper, textiles, glass, aluminium, steel and other metals. Moreover, the collection, sorting and marketing of waste material could provide an income for the community, although recycling must not be seen solely as a profit-making venture.

In a world whose resources are finite, it is simply unacceptable that large quantities of materials that could be reused or recycled end up on dump sites. Recycling programmes could so easily change urban waste from being the cause of problems to being a source of essential materials. Given the consequences for the environment of dumping and incineration, recycling is a necessity rather than an option.

Environmental trial by fire ...
In an attempt to reduce the volume of waste at this dump (below far left), fires burn uncontrolled, releasing toxic vapours into the air.

... and by water
Rubbish festers in a pool (below left), from which contaminated water may seep down to affect local drinking water supplies.

The mounting problem
The quantities of coastal rubbish are now so great that some birds such as this osprey (right) build their nests almost entirely from artificial materials.

The sea returns our waste
Plastic washed up on a Cretan beach (below): all rubbish is unsightly, but some proves lethal to wildlife.

CLEANING UP THE MED

It could be that too little is done too late to save the Mediterranean. But there is a solution that offers economic as well as environmental advantages – a practical concept known as 'clean production'.

Clean production methods – the principles of which can be applied to all forms of agriculture as well as to industry – eliminate hazardous or otherwise damaging waste and products and use a minimal amount of raw materials, water and energy. Commodities produced by 'clean' methods do not damage the environment at any stage of their cycle.

Clean industry

The concept of clean production embraces product design and manufacture; raw material selection, extraction and processing; the product's use in industry or the household; and its reintroduction into the production cycle at the end of its use. Clean production does not mean simply reducing the volume of waste after it has been produced, for instance by incineration. Nor does it mean diluting pollutants by discharging them into water or the air.

Clean production emphasizes more than technology alone. For instance, instead of using a hazardous substance and then looking for ways to deal with the pollution it creates, companies should seek out a different raw material, which does not create the pollution; as an example, some new processes use water as a solvent instead of halogenated hydrocarbons, which is both safer and cheaper. With clean production, material that has previously been regarded as waste may become a valuable resource. Sewage is a case in point: if clean production were adopted and harmful substances no longer discharged into the sewers, sewage sludge could safely be used as a fertilizer.

If the aims of clean production are to be achieved, all aspects of a product must be assessed to be sure that it does not damage the environment. But this does not mean only that goods should not be hazardous; they should also be durable and reusable, efficient in any use of energy, and be easy to repair and refurbish.

The essential requirement for successfully applying clean production is that people should be aware of how much waste they produce. To begin with, companies should carry out an audit to measure both the raw materials used and the products or waste created, which clarifies the type and quantity of toxic chemicals present at all stages. These should then be replaced with non-toxic substances, and a different, safer production process should be used where appropriate.

Co-operative ventures between research institutes and small- or medium-sized companies in some of the most polluting sectors of industry have produced remarkable results in this area. In one Swedish town, Landskrona, a light engineering firm found that they could substitute lubricating mineral oils with vegetable-based oils, and use powder-based paints instead of solvent-based ones, with a total saving of $440,000 a year. A chemical company discovered that 3 percent of their raw material was inadvertently discharged as waste, amounting to a loss of $300,000 a year.

Such case studies demonstrate that clean production can bring economic savings. But the really significant savings result because clean production methods avoid the enormous costs associated with treatment and disposal of toxic waste, as well as those that arise, for example, when waste leaks from a landfill site and contaminates a water supply. The greatest benefit that would come from clean production, however, is that the social costs of a degraded environment and the resulting cancers, lung and liver diseases would be much reduced. We can hardly afford not to implement clean production.

The challenge to growth
This view of Algiers provides dramatic evidence of the unprecedented migration to coastal cities that has taken place in the Mediterranean over the last 30 years. This has been coupled with a massive building programme and a remarkable change in lifestyle for many people. Until recently the response to the environmental problems this created was piecemeal and temporary. Now, as local services and wildlife alike are overwhelmed, a more mature way of thinking is needed – one that accepts that we cannot carry on squandering resources, or rely on the hope that the waste we produce will simply disappear. The means of giving practical form to this urgent need are encompassed in the concept of 'clean production'.

Ecological agriculture

Two major kinds of pollution are associated with intensive agrochemical farming: one is created by pesticides; the other is eutrophication or over-enrichment of rivers and seas by chemical fertilizers and effluent from intensive livestock units.

The pollution caused by pesticides, plus the increasing resistance of the pests to them, means that alternatives must rapidly be found. 'Insurance' spraying, whereby crops are routinely dosed with large amounts of pesticides 'just in case' pests should arrive, aggravates both of these problems and is one of the most damaging and wasteful aspects of agrochemical farming.

'Ecological' techniques (those of organic farming, for example) are based on the study of natural ecosystems which, unlike crops, are rarely devastated by diseases and pests. These biological techniques include mixing crops in a way that slows down the spread of pests; breeding back into plants natural deterrents such as downy leaves and sticky hairs, and assisting spiders, insects and parasites to control the population of pests. Traditional methods of cultivation such as crop rotation when combined with these new techniques can also combat pests and diseases.

In circumstances where biological techniques have not yet been perfected, 'integrated pest management' (IPM), which uses ecological practices in conjunction with pesticides only as a last resort, may be an appropriate transitional phase. (It must be stressed, however, that this is not IPM as promoted by chemical companies, who apply the term in a way that emphasizes the use of their products while paying only lip service to the importance of other aspects.)

Switching to true ecological practices would also help to solve the problems caused by nutrients. In some cases it is possible to integrate crop and livestock farming using field rotation, which would remove the need for expensive artificial fertilizers. Similar benefits would come from a return to

Waste not, want not
This irrigation system in Israel uses processed material from the local sewage works. This makes good use of limited water resources, and helps to ensure that nutrients in sewage are incorporated back into crops rather than creating a problem in rivers and sea. The result is a better environment and a more profitable farm.

using locally produced manure. Unlike artificial fertilizers, manure releases nutrients steadily, and the plant material mixed with the animal dung adds bulk to the soil, helping to prevent erosion.

Animal slurry from intensive livestock units could also be used for manure or be treated at a sewage plant and then returned to the soil. If the supply exceeds demand then it is, perhaps, time for the farmers to address the question of whether it is really necessary to rear livestock in this way, which is, in any case, a very inefficient method of producing protein.

Plans for urban sewage works should also try to ensure that they can supply fertilizer to agriculture, rather than discharging nutrients to the sea. Again, this does of course require that industry introduce clean production.

Alternative agriculture pays

There has been no systematic survey of ecological agricultural techniques across the Mediterranean region, but studies in the United States show that alternative methods, generating real profits and creating real benefits, exist for crops that are also grown in the Mediterranean. For example, breeding resistance to disease back into wheat, corn and alfalfa cost $9.3 million, yet the increased yields alone were worth several million dollars annually, even

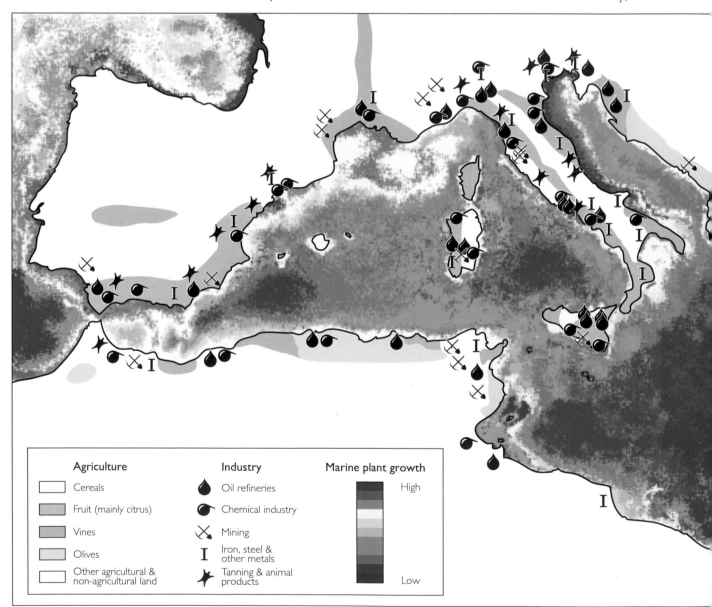

Agriculture		Industry		Marine plant growth	
☐	Cereals	🛢	Oil refineries		High
▨	Fruit (mainly citrus)	🛢	Chemical industry		
▨	Vines	✕	Mining		
▨	Olives	I	Iron, steel & other metals		
☐	Other agricultural & non-agricultural land	✦	Tanning & animal products		Low

without taking into account the money saved by using fewer pesticides. Similarly, 48 percent of cotton in the USA is now grown using predictive monitoring rather than insurance spraying, with a 20–30 percent increase in yield, and a 30–40 percent saving in pest control costs. Mixed crop and livestock farms consistently combine lower expenditure and the use of fewer chemicals with significantly greater profits, and their relatively small scale makes them ideal for Mediterranean conditions.

The Mediterranean states have no choice but to introduce alternative agricultural techniques. Present methods are expensive, and destroy the environment. Techniques such as biological control, recycling nutrients, and teaching monitoring skills cost comparatively little. They give similar or better yields, and they drastically reduce the amount needing to be spent on imported chemicals, while raising the value of crops for export.

In order to move towards both ecological agriculture and clean industry the Mediterranean countries must now establish contacts with researchers and producers throughout the rest of the world. Armed with good information and supported by appropriate funds, nations, companies and individuals can take the philosophy of clean production, modify the practice to fit the Mediterranean context, and make the sea healthy once more.

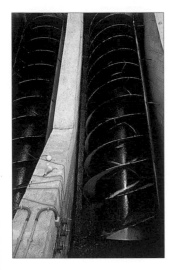

New but wrong
Even new sewage works continue to ignore the need to stop nutrient discharges.

Mediterranean synopsis
The map shows five of the major sources of industrial pollution in the Mediterranean – the chemical industry, oil refineries, metal production, mining and tanning. Also shown are the main types of crop – cereals, olives, vines and other fruit – all of which use fertilizers and pesticides to varying degrees and all of which, together with livestock, contaminate the sea to some extent.
In the sea itself, the different colours represent the varying amounts of phytoplankton in the surface waters, from sparse growth (blue) through yellow to maximum (red), due to a combination of natural nutrients and nutrient pollution from industry, sewage effluent and agriculture. Particularly noticeable are the generally high levels of growth near the coast, the over-rich plume of the Rhône, the Adriatic, the northern Aegean, the coast of eastern Egypt and the Bay of Tunis (which may be linked to phosphate mining). The information on phytoplankton growth is based on a false-colour composite satellite image produced by a scanner on NASA's Nimbus-7 research satellite. There are no specific images that give clues about other forms of pollution, but these are likely to have a similar distribution to that of nutrients shown here.

DOLPHINS AND WHALES

There are about a dozen species of cetacean in the Mediterranean, including the fin whale (*Balaenoptera physalus*, the second largest species in the world, and the sperm whale (*Physeter macrocephalus*) as well as the common and striped dolphin (*Delphinus delphis* and *Stenella coeruleoalba*) and the bottlenose dolphin (*Tursiops truncatus*).

Many populations of these marine mammals are in a steady and alarming decline, which could ultimately lead to their extinction in many regions. They are protected in several Mediterranean countries, but still there are few effective measures to ensure that they survive. Various international bodies and organizations, as well as different conventions, have repeatedly voiced their concern for the future of cetaceans in the Mediterranean Sea. Yet all this concern has not moved governments to action.

Victims of pollution?

The special characteristics of marine mammals – their fat-rich blubber layers where pollutants accumulate, and their position at the top of the food chain – make them particularly vulnerable to changes in their environment, and many scientists consider them to be particularly sensitive indicators of marine pollution. Organochlorine compounds (such as DDT and PCBs) have been shown to interfere with reproduction in marine mammals, which have a naturally low reproductive rate. Some scientists have predicted that marine mammals living in highly polluted waters could become locally extinct.

Some complex organic compounds such as the organochlorines are known to suppress the immune system in some species, making animals far more susceptible to disease. The death of thousands of striped dolphins in the western Mediterranean since 1990 is likely to have been the result of disease in dolphins that were already weakened by high concentrations of compounds such as PCBs in their bodies.

Dolphins that died in 1990 were found to contain levels of PCBs between 400 and 500 ppm, soaring to 2,800 ppm in one individual. The dolphins were also contaminated by heavy metals: more than 800 ppm of mercury were found in the liver, and over 100 ppm in the brain (the WHO considers that over 1 ppm of mercury renders food unfit for human consumption).

Oil pollution threatens cetaceans too, either directly through physical contact, possibly leading to the blockage of their blow holes, or indirectly, if they eat contaminated fish. And the oil industry is believed to cause other, less obvious but equally serious, effects: the rigs destroy habitats and the noise of exploration and extraction drives the animals away.

Going solo
A striped dolphin (*Stenella coeruleoalba*, right) reveals its distinctive blue and white markings as it leaps clear of the water. Striped dolphins are the only species to be affected by the viral disease that has contributed to the deaths of an estimated 6,000 animals in the Mediterranean since the summer of 1990.

A sea of dolphins
Common dolphins (*Delphinus delphis*, below) 'porpoise' in the open sea. These dolphins form large schools and are most frequently seen off the coast of Africa – although their numbers have declined in recent years.

Hunting and fishing

Overfishing is another factor affecting cetaceans in the Mediterranean. As their food becomes scarce, the cetaceans may in turn become fewer in number; those that survive may suffer malnutrition, resulting in parasitic infections, disease and reduced fertility. The large fleet fishing in Mediterranean waters – and in particular the use of driftnets, which spread rapidly from Italy to Spain, Tunisia, Greece, France and Morocco – also increases the risk of cetaceans getting caught accidentally in nets.

The fishermen themselves are responsible for the death of a large number of dolphins, which they regard as rivals in the hunt for a scarce resource: the dolphins are often accused of spoiling fishing gear and nets when they attempt to take fish from them. Every year, dolphins appear stranded on the coast with bruises or bullet wounds and their tail fin severed.

Dolphins form part of the history and mythology of every Mediterranean culture. But the poor condition of the marine ecosystem has led to their disappearance from many areas. The carcasses washed up on the Mediterranean shores are strong evidence that decisive action to protect these creatures – and their habitat – must be taken without delay.

A dolphin 'smile'
The familiar features of a bottlenose dolphin (*Tursiops truncatus*, above). The cone-shaped teeth enable the dolphin to grab hold of slippery fish and swallow them whole.

Marine giant
A fin whale (*Balaenoptera physalus*, below) ploughs through the sea, its blow hole just visible in front of the wave. At up to 25 metres long, this is one of the largest whales.

COUNTRY FILES

LIBYA

al-Jamahiriyah al-Arabiya al-Libya al-Shabiya al-Ishtirakiya
Socialist People's Libyan Arab Jamahiriyah

AREA 1,759,540 sq km. LENGTH OF COASTLINE 1,700 km.
POPULATION 4,280,000.

'Jamahiriyah' means 'state of the masses'; Libya is a
republic whose head of state is called the Leader of the
Revolution. The only permitted political party is the
Arab Socialist Union Organization.

THE PEOPLE
The people of Libya are mainly Arab, with some
Berbers living in the west, and nomadic people of
Berber origin in the south west. Some 97% of the
population is Sunni Muslim; Islam is crucial in Libyan
domestic and international politics. The vast majority of
Libyans live on or near the coast; about 20% of the
population is concentrated around Tripoli.

THE ECONOMY
LABOUR FORCE 18% in agriculture, 31% in industry,
27% in services, 24% in government.
MAJOR EXPORT Petroleum (1 million barrels per day).
MAJOR IMPORTS Machinery, food, manufactured goods.
MINERAL RESOURCES Oil, natural gas, gypsum.
CHIEF CROPS Cereals, olives, dates, citrus fruit, peanuts.
VEHICLES 334,000 commercial, 428,000 cars.

THE ENVIRONMENT
THE PRESENT Libya suffers from severe oil pollution and
the coast is covered in tar balls. A major problem faces
Libyan agriculture, as the irrigated land is now largely
saline, owing to over-exploitation of the subterranean
aquifers that collect rain water. Sea water has reportedly
reached as far as 20 km inland around Tripoli.
However, marine life thrives in Libyan waters as local
fishing is minimal, and fishing by outsiders is
controlled by the Libyan government. There is one
national park, in the north east of the country.
THE FUTURE Libyan land ecology could well be altered
dramatically by the government's water pipeline,
designed to correct the water shortage in the narrow
fertile coastal strip by exploiting aquifers beneath the
Sahara up to 900 km from the coast.

EGYPT

al Jumhuriyat Misr al-Arabiya
Arab Republic of Egypt

AREA 1,001,449 sq km. MEDITERRANEAN COAST 900 km.
POPULATION 54,700,000.

Egypt is a republic, with a popularly elected legislature.
The President is head of state and appoints a Council of
Ministers to form the government.

THE PEOPLE
About 98% of Egyptians live in the Nile valley and
delta; an estimated 14 million (25%) live in the capital,
Cairo, and a further 5 million in Alexandria, the
country's chief port. Nomadic or semi-nomadic
Bedouin live in the desert and on the fringes of the
towns. The population will probably double by 2015.
A low rate of literacy makes TV and radio important
media; free speech is constitutionally guaranteed.

THE ECONOMY
LABOUR FORCE 44% in agriculture, 22% in services, 14%
in industry.
MAJOR EXPORTS Petroleum (60-65% of total exports),
cotton, oranges, rice, cement, textiles.
MAJOR IMPORTS Food, machinery, fertilizers, wood.
MINERAL RESOURCES Oil, phosphates, gypsum, iron,
manganese, limestone.
CHIEF CROPS Cotton (one of the largest producers at
400,000 tonnes annually), maize, rice, wheat, beans.
VEHICLES 371,000 commercial, 783,000 cars.

THE ENVIRONMENT
THE PRESENT Oil pollution is intense all along Egypt's
Mediterranean coast. Industrial plants discharge more
than 2 million tonnes of waste water into the sea each
day; this is contaminated with chlorine, oil, cadmium
and mercury; raw sewage dumped from Alexandria
arrives in important fish breeding grounds.
The promised benefits of the Aswan High Dam have
not materialized – the extent of fertile land has actually
decreased, resulting in heavy use of pesticides,
herbicides and fertilizers – although hydroelectricity
from Aswan has brought power to much of the
country. Most Egyptian environmentalists consider
pesticides to be one of the major problems: Egypt
imports nearly 17,500 tonnes of pesticides annually, and
some widely used herbicides are extremely hazardous.
Ships carrying toxic and radioactive waste use the Suez
Canal frequently. Egypt has four marine and coastal
protected areas.
THE FUTURE A Green Party has recently been officially
recognized, but is pro-nuclear. Sympathy for
environmental issues is high, at least among influential
academics. However, tourism both to Egypt's ancient
inland sites and to its Mediterranean coast is increasing,
and a nuclear power station is planned.

MALTA

Repubblika Ta' Malta
Republic of Malta

AREA 316 sq km including Gozo (67 sq km) and islets.
LENGTH OF COASTLINE 300 km. **POPULATION** 400,000.

Malta is a parliamentary democracy. Elections are by proportional representation. A Prime Minister is head of the government; the President is head of state.

THE PEOPLE

Malta became independent in 1964, and a republic in 1974. The Maltese include Arab, French and Italian ethnic groups. Most live in the east of the island, which contains the capital, Valletta (pop. 15,000).

THE ECONOMY

LABOUR FORCE 35% in industry and commerce, 30% in services, 22% in government, 4.5% in agriculture and fisheries, with many part-time farmers.
MAJOR EXPORTS Ships, textiles, yarns, manufactured goods. Tourism is a major source of income.
MAJOR IMPORTS Manufactured goods, machinery, transport equipment.
MINERAL RESOURCES Limestone, salt.
CHIEF CROPS Tomatoes, potatoes, onions, cabbages, fruit.
VEHICLES 18,000 commercial, 85,000 cars.

THE ENVIRONMENT

THE PRESENT Most sewage is untreated. The one coal-fired power station has no filters; although a cleaner one is planned, the issue is controversial. Hunting is nominally licensed, but shooting is common even in bird sanctuaries. There are two nature reserves. Fishing catches include sea turtles, which are openly sold, coral fishing is being developed, and fishermen actively 'defend themselves' against dolphins. Use of herbicides and pesticides is increasing.
THE FUTURE Urbanization at the present rate will both reduce agricultural land and contribute to soil erosion. A huge tourist complex planned for Gozo will cover roughly one third of the island. Demands on local resources will therefore increase dramatically, while the scheme will destroy unique habitats.

CYPRUS

Kypriaki Dimokratia/Kibris Cumhuriyeti
Republic of Cyprus

AREA 9251 sq km. **LENGTH OF COASTLINE** 800 km.
POPULATION 696,000.

Cyprus is a parliamentary democracy; but Turkey invaded the island in 1974 and, in 1983, declared the northern sector the Turkish Republic of North Cyprus (recognized only by Turkey). Negotiations to reunite the island politically are currently deadlocked.

THE PEOPLE

Greek Cypriots comprise 78% of the population, and Turkish nearly 19%. Since partition in 1974, most Turkish Cypriots have lived in the north. One fifth of the population lives in Nicosia, the capital city.

THE ECONOMY

LABOUR FORCE 21% in agriculture, 20% in industry, 18% in commerce, 19% in services.
MAJOR EXPORTS Clothing, machinery. Considerable income is also derived from 1 million tourists annually.
MAJOR IMPORTS Manufactured goods, machinery, transportation equipment, petrol, food.
MINERAL RESOURCES Copper, asbestos, gypsum, building stone, marble, clay, salt.
CHIEF CROPS Cereals, citrus fruit, grapes, olives.
VEHICLES 54,000 commercial, 142,000 cars.

THE ENVIRONMENT

THE PRESENT The ever-increasing tourist trade threatens the remaining sea-turtle nesting beaches, but local communities are anxious to develop a share in tourist wealth. Cyprus is a haven for migrating birds, but dam-building threatens the wetlands they use. There are two nature reserves, which are coastal wetlands. A small community of monk seals apparently survives. Sponge fishing ceased in 1986, after an unidentified disease struck the sponges. Industrial pollution of the sea is relatively low, but pesticides are liberally used. Sewage treatment plants are under construction. A third power station is planned, against local protests; almost all Cypriot houses heat water by solar power.
THE FUTURE In general, the Cypriot government has a good record for ecological concern. A promise to protect Akamas beach (a turtle nesting ground) was made in 1990. The major threat to the environment is from tourism and its demands on natural resources, food and energy supplies. Cyprus does have an 'open ticket' to join the European Community, however, and membership would increase pressure for conservation and anti-pollution measures.

A Maltese speciality

These limestone blocks in Marsaxlokk harbour, Malta (left), are not for building but for fishing. They are used as weights for palm fronds, and are dropped overboard out at sea. Fish are drawn to the shade that the plants provide, and so become easy prey for fishermen.

LIBYA, EGYPT AND THE ISLAND STATES

More than nine tenths of Libya is a flat, arid, sand and rock desert – there are mountains only in the extreme south – and even on the coast rainfall is slight and erratic. There are no permanent rivers at all. Average temperatures are high everywhere, and reach 49°C in summer in the south. Less than 2 percent of Libya is arable, and only a tenth of that is irrigated.

Most of Egypt too is flat, although there are mountains in the south west, on the Red Sea coast and southern Sinai. Egyptian geography is dominated by the river Nile, and by the desert – sandy to the west of the Nile, and stony, riven by wadis, to the east. Most of Egypt's cultivable land lies along the banks of the Nile and in the 15,500 square kilometres of the Nile delta. Only the area around Alexandria enjoys even moderate rainfall.

Malta's interior is hilly rather than mountainous, and the climate is typically Mediterranean. The island, especially the coast, is being urbanized rapidly even by Mediterranean standards: half the land was farmed in 198, whereas today only a third is cultivated.

Most of Cyprus – the Mediterranean's third largest island – consists of a fertile plain, lying between the Troodos mountains in the south and the Kyrenians in the north; nearly half the land is arable, and there are numerous rivers in all but the northeastern tip. Rain is plentiful in winter, but may not fall at all in summer.

Special reserve
Thousands of greater flamingos (above) live on Lake Bardawil in eastern Egypt.

Growing on stony ground
The view at Akamas Bay (right) reveals the fertility and barrenness of Cyprus.

Past and future
Horses still pull ploughs on Malta (above), where part-time farming is widespread. But tourism and urbanization may disrupt this way of life for ever.

River of life
For thousands of years, the Nile (right) has nourished those living along the 1,550 kilometres of its banks in Egypt. Yet the desert is always visible just beyond the rich vegetation that lines the river – a stark reminder of how vulnerable is the fertility of the Nile valley.

Between the desert and the deep blue sea
Only a tiny percentage of Libya's land (above) is fertile, and much of that is intractable scrub. To make matters worse, fresh water reserves are so depleted that aquifers are now contaminated by the sea.

NUCLEAR ISSUES
MILITARY MIGHT AND CIVIL POWER

I N MARCH 1946, the US battleship *Missouri* brought back to Istanbul the body of the Turkish ambassador in Washington. That demonstration of support for Turkey, under supposed threat from Soviet expansion, was the unofficial start of the so-called Truman Doctrine intended to prevent the spread of communism in the Mediterranean. Two years later, the US warships operating in the Mediterranean were named the Sixth Fleet – a sign of their permanent presence in the sea. In the early 1950s the first US tactical (short-range) naval nuclear weapon ever sent overseas went to the Mediterranean. Since then, the Mediterranean has not been free of nuclear weapons for a single minute. In the 1960s, the Soviet, French and British navies became nuclear-armed, and they are permanently operating in the Mediterranean.

Nuclear weapons were seen by the superpowers as the cure for all the conflicts of the Mediterranean region. In reality, they have become part of the sickness. Despite their presence, the Mediterranean people have witnessed an endless round of conflicts in the last 40 years: confrontations between East and West, differences between North and South, regional territorial disputes, acts of terrorism. Because of superpower rivalry, the possibility that local tensions will escalate into nuclear conflict has cast its shadow over the region since the Second World War.

By the 1980s, nearly one third of the world's nuclear arsenal was at sea, naval nuclear weapons were not part of the arms control programme, the maritime strategies of the nuclear navies were very aggressive and nuclear navies were involved in several conventional conflicts. In the Mediterranean, in the 1980s, between 60 and 70 nuclear-capable warships, including submarines, were in day-to-day operation. Some of these ships, between 12 and 20 of them, were nuclear-powered as well. All together, the naval nuclear arsenal in the Mediterranean amounts to 1,000 weapons. Besides the four nuclear fleets, France and Israel have land-based nuclear weapons and the US store nuclear weapons in Greece, Turkey and Italy.

The explosive sea
Air, missile and naval bases, and nuclear weapons' stores, ring the Mediterranean. Since 1948 the USA has had an entire fleet permanently stationed in the Mediterranean and has made a heavy investment in air and naval bases, while the UK has had a military presence in the area for at least two centuries. With France, these powers now maintain a nuclear capability in the Mediterranean that the USSR has 'balanced' with its own seaborne nuclear forces. Lacking permanent naval bases in the Mediterranean outside Syria, the Soviet navy has adopted a number of shallow-water sites as habitual anchorages. Adding to the dangers posed by the 'official' nuclear powers, several Middle Eastern countries are believed to be developing, or have developed, nuclear weapons.

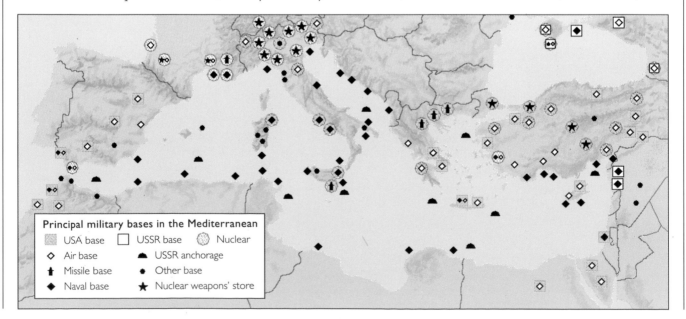

Principal military bases in the Mediterranean

The invisible war
The British nuclear submarine HMS *Swiftsure* surfaces in the Mediterranean (left). The underwater fleets of the major powers remain on a permanent war footing while submerged, so increasing the risk of accident. Environmentalists have also claimed that the ageing reactors in some nuclear submarines are now increasing the risk of accident at sea.

The people's choice?
The US navy base at La Maddalena, Sardinia (above), has been used by nuclear-armed submarines since 1985 – contrary to assurances by both US and Italian authorities. The majority of the population of Sardinia is opposed to the nuclear presence at the base, but the regional government's planned referendum on the issue was declared unconstitutional by the Italian high courts.

The safety record of nuclear weapons in the Mediterranean is very poor. Between 1945 and 1990 the nuclear fleets were involved in 110 accidents; nuclear-propelled warships were affected in 15 of these. The most potentially dangerous accident occurred in November 1975 when the US aircraft carrier *J.F. Kennedy* and the US cruiser *Belknap*, both with nuclear arms on board, collided during naval exercises near Sicily. Fires broke out on both ships and there was a series of explosions aboard the *Belknap*. A 'broken arrow' alarm was given, declaring a possible accident involving nuclear weapons, but the missiles escaped the fire. Besides that, two capsules containing material for nuclear weapons have been lost on the seabed since 1956, when a US military aircraft sank in the Mediterranean.

The Mediterranean Sea is surrounded by military bases, which provide communications links between warships and central commands and often store nuclear weapons; some have important implications, in that they reveal the strength of the host country's political allegiance. The US military bases in particular have been used for NATO 'out-of-area' operations, for supporting the rapid deployment forces of the US Central Command and for

The future in their hands
Egyptian soldiers watch as the nuclear-powered USS *Dwight D. Eisenhower* slips though the Suez Canal, carrying aircraft and nuclear weapons to enforce the blockade of Iraq in August 1990 in the run-up to the Gulf war. As long as conflicts plague the Middle East, it is unlikely that the Mediterranean will be free of the nuclear threat.

The French connection
At the French air base at Istres, a navy helicopter hovers near Mirage jets, assembled ready to move to the Gulf in September 1990. The Istres base contains a store of nuclear weapons, and the Mirages are capable of delivering them.

applying political pressure in the southern flank of NATO. The American infrastructure in the Mediterranean was fundamental to the recent rapid deployment of troops and equipment in the Gulf region.

Nuclear warships call in at many harbours all around the Mediterranean. These 'courtesy' visits are seen as a form of diplomacy; but, while seeking support for the nuclear presence, they ignore the risks of introducing nuclear weapons and reactors into the heart of densely populated harbours. None of the Mediterranean states has effective legislation against nuclear weapons. Malta, for example, has declared itself a nuclear-free zone, but has no measures to guarantee this is respected. Spain has banned nuclear weapons in its territory, but still allows nuclear warships to enter its harbours.

Too many weapons, too little commitment

Politicians – both Mediterranean and non-Mediterranean – have admitted that there are too many weapons in this sea. However, the Mediterranean states themselves have not made a strong enough commitment to bring about a reduction of forces, particularly nuclear forces, in the sea, nor are they applying any pressure internationally for this to happen. None of the proposals to reduce the superpowers' fleets has ever been put into effect: although the Soviet Union has announced its intention to remove its nuclear warships from the Mediterranean, they are still operating in its waters. Both France and the United States are very reluctant to accept naval arms control, especially in the Mediterranean. All nuclear powers continue to site their weapons there. The fall of the Berlin Wall has not, it seems, had much effect in the area. Moreover, the war in the Gulf will cast a long shadow, making it more difficult to eliminate nuclear weapons from the Mediterranean region.

There is an increasingly strong need to approach Mediterranean security problems from a common and wide perspective. International co-operation should go beyond military agreements and exercises, and embrace economic, social and environmental issues too. Only in such a context will the trust among nations be strengthened, and the removal of nuclear weapons be possible. And only then will we be more certain to achieve the goal of peace.

NUCLEAR POWER

During the 1960s and 1970s, when nuclear energy was the rising star of industry in many countries, a huge number of nuclear power plants were planned. Of the Mediterranean countries, only France produces the greater proportion of the electricity it needs by nuclear energy. Others have tried to do the same, but with little or no success.

Earthquake-prone Italy has very little 'safe' territory in which to site nuclear reactors, and there is a good deal of public opposition to nuclear power: a national referendum in 1987, the year after the Chernobyl disaster, led to the closure of Italy's three nuclear power stations. Because of its political isolation, Libya has not been able to build a single commercial reactor. Spain had planned more than 35 reactors for the 1990s but has now abandoned most of these; in 1984 the government stopped the construction of five plants, because of the crippling debts incurred; in 1989, after an old gas-cooled reactor was badly damaged in a fire, only nine reactors were in operation. Greece still has no commercial nuclear reactors (it does have two research reactors) and has no plans for any. Turkey and Egypt so far have been unable to afford the nuclear plants they want. Israel operates a French research reactor and reprocessing plant, but has been unable to buy a commercial reactor, largely due to objections lodged by the USA because Israel has refused to sign the Nuclear Non-Proliferation Treaty.

Radiation in the Mediterranean

Nuclear power has been promoted as cheap, safe, efficient and, recently, even as clean and capable of stopping global warming. Unfortunately, exactly the opposite has been demonstrated.

Nuclear power is not clean – nor is it safe. During normal operation, every plant discharges radioactive gases, liquids and solids. In one year, a single plant pumps billions of becquerels of radioactivity into the air, the rivers or the sea. Uncontrolled and accidental discharges – from faulty equipment such as leaking steam generators and condensers – are also quite frequent. The radioactive gases accumulate in the atmosphere: little is known of their long-term effects. The liquids and particles (containing radioactive products such as caesium-137, cobalt-60 and even plutonium) enter the water and sediments of the rivers and the sea, from where they can enter the food chain.

Hazard warning
The symbol above is internationally recognized as a warning of the presence of nuclear radiation and its hazards. The three 'arms' represent the three kinds of lethal emissions – alpha, beta and gamma – that are given off by radioactive materials and by a nuclear explosion.

The nuclear dream?
A nuclear power station broods over the Rhône valley in France. Nearly two thirds of the country's electricity is supplied by nuclear energy and the French nuclear programme has been presented as an outstanding example of how to provide electricity at cheap prices. But the industry runs at a huge loss and has built up a massive foreign debt to finance its nuclear investment.

On the sunny side
Solar panels cover rooftop after rooftop in Tel Aviv, Israel. Such panels may be passive, concentrating the heat from sunlight onto water whose flow is controlled by gravity; or photovoltaic, in which the heat of the sun acts on the molecular structure of silicon to produce an electric current. This can then be used to heat water or power electric lighting. Both systems are ideal alternative energy sources for the Mediterranean, which enjoys constant sunshine for much of the year.

Seaweeds can accumulate radioactive substances, sometimes to thousands of times the background levels. Radioactive contamination also builds up in shellfish, fish and crabs. This is then passed up through the food chain, to birds, mammals and people. Different isotopes accumulate in different parts of the body. Iodine-131 becomes concentrated in the thyroid; strontium-90, caesium-137, plutonium-239 and americium-241 are deposited in bone; magnesium-54 accumulates in the liver, ruthenium-106 in the lower intestine. These and other radioactive substances cause diseases such as leukaemia and cancer of the thyroid, lungs or breast. Perhaps most sinister is the genetic damage they cause, which is passed on to future generations.

Most of these discharges could be within 'official' limits (set by the industry), but they can hardly be checked, and no one knows if they are safe. In the past, some discharges have been authorized as perfectly safe, only to be prohibited after damaging effects have become apparent at much lower levels. Many specialists now believe that there is no safe level of radiation.

These daily discharges are a huge cause for concern, yet they would be dwarfed should there be a major accident, such as a 'meltdown' of a reactor core (which the nuclear industry claimed was impossible – until Chernobyl). A few hundred kilometres would prove no obstacle to a radioactive cloud, while the release of radioactive material from a catastrophic accident into the waters of the enclosed Mediterranean Sea could have horrific consequences.

Radioactive waste, emitting different levels of radiation, results from all stages of the production of nuclear power, and easily amounts to tens of thousands of cubic metres in the lifetime of any one nuclear plant. There is no means of disposing of this waste; it can only be stored, on site, in such a way that best prevents the escape of radioactive materials (some of which may remain dangerous for thousands of years). The biggest and virtually insoluble problem is the spent fuel that is periodically removed from the reactor core. This is still intensely radioactive; it is also very hot and must be cooled for months before it can even be transported to an 'interim' storage site or to a reprocessing plant. But reprocessing only postpones the decision about what to do with the waste, and actually increases the total amount produced. On the other hand, no secure place for 'high-level' waste has ever been found: no known technology can guarantee the complete isolation of this material from the environment for hundreds of thousands of years.

Nuclear power in the greenhouse age

As the debate over global warming (the 'greenhouse effect') has intensified, some have argued that nuclear power represents the solution to the problem, because it produces almost none of those gases that are building up in the atmosphere and leading to global warming. But, again, the nuclear promise is a false one. Although around half the contributions to the greenhouse effect are related to the use of fossil fuels, nuclear power could replace only those used to generate electricity. As greenhouse gases and carbon dioxide in particular come from many sources other than electricity production, replacing fossil fuel power stations with nuclear ones would address only about 10 percent of the problem. The huge expansion of the nuclear industry that this would require would drain the resources of even rich, industrialized countries – and simply could not be considered by poorer nations.

Measures to use energy more efficiently and to reduce the amount of energy used could be put into effect far more cheaply – and quickly. Other, 'renewable', sources of energy hold greater promise for generating clean, inexpensive electricity – all without any of the major risks to health and safety that are associated with nuclear power.

The safer alternative

The move towards the safer alternative of using renewable energy sources must include both energy conservation and energy efficiency. The methods used to convert gas, coal, oil or uranium to electricity, for example, are scandalously inefficient, with about two thirds of the 'primary' energy being wasted in the form of residual heat. Yet this wasted energy could be used to provide heating and hot water for homes and industries. Making equipment that uses electricity more efficient too could bring a huge reduction in the demand, so cutting energy needs as well as emissions of greenhouse gases. The technologies to reduce the amount of energy we consume already exist – and it makes far more sense for governments to take up these cheaper and cleaner options than to look for ways of producing yet more energy.

At the same time, renewable sources of energy such as wind, wave and solar power and biomass fuel (from plants) could replace uranium and fossil fuels. Even on a direct comparison of the prices of installation and equipment, renewables are becoming competitive with conventional energy sources, leaving aside the 'hidden' cost of environmental damage from fossil fuels and uranium, which remains the real price we pay for using them.

Some countries around the Mediterranean are experimenting with the use of renewable resources, but the funds provided for research are very low compared to those for nuclear power. (This is in spite of the excellent geographical location of these countries with regard to solar energy: in the region as a whole, the solar energy potential lies between 1,100 and 2,200 kilowatt hours per square metre per year.) Nevertheless, in Israel for example 60 percent of homes are equipped with passive solar energy panels, allowing the sun to heat water; and in Spain some 20,000 photovoltaic solar installations produce electricity directly from the sun. Of all Mediterranean countries, the poorest nations would benefit most from exploring energy-saving technologies and renewable sources of energy, not least because they would avoid the expensive mistakes of the 'developed' nations of the world.

The warmth of the Earth
Geothermal power stations, like this one (below left) in Tuscany, Italy, offer a way to heat water without using fossil fuels or nuclear power. Geothermal energy may be 'wet' or 'dry'. The 'wet' method uses hot water produced by volcanic activity; using 'dry' energy involves pumping water deep under ground, where it heats at the rate of about 30°C for every kilometre of depth, then returning it to the surface. These processes use no fuel, but there may be more subtle costs if unsightly pipes are allowed to disfigure the landscape, and their potential impact on the environment warrants greater scrutiny.

Winds of change
Windmills on the plain of Lasithi in Crete (above) have been used to help to irrigate this high plateau for generations. The past has a lesson for the future here – the driving force of the wind costs nothing, and modern aerodynamics, together with effective systems of energy storage to ensure a constant supply, can make it a highly efficient energy source for a number of applications.

AIR POLLUTION
WARMING UP THE EARTH

GLOBAL WARMING, caused by the accumulation of heat-trapping 'greenhouse' gases in the atmosphere, is probably the most serious threat facing the environment today. No one can predict exactly what will happen, but most scientists in the field agree on some likely results. Rising seas are expected to flood low-lying coastal areas, with devastating effects. Agricultural land and fresh water supplies may be contaminated by salt; and, although rainfall will increase in some areas, it will decrease in others, perhaps causing widespread water shortages.

There is little doubt that some warming will occur. In a report issued in May 1990 by the UN Intergovernmental Panel on Climatic Change (IPCC), over 300 of the world's leading climatologists stated: 'We are certain that emissions resulting from human activities are substantially increasing the atmospheric concentrations of the greenhouse gases.... These increases will enhance the greenhouse effect, resulting ... in an additional warming of the Earth's surface.' Moreover, the scientists concluded that natural 'feedbacks' triggered by global warming are likely to reinforce the warming trend.

Fouling the air

Atmospheric pollution has long been identified as one of the principal causes of environmental degradation. In cities of the Mediterranean – as elsewhere – the main scourge of the atmosphere is the automobile. In Spain alone, in

Signs of the times
Gases from vehicle exhausts (above) and from industrial complexes like this one in Israel (below) are two of the major sources of atmospheric pollution contributing to the 'greenhouse effect'. Unless radical steps are taken to reduce and eventually stop such emissions, the Earth's temperature will increase at a rate unknown in the history of human civilization.

1988, there were more than 14 million cars. Their exhausts discharge massive quantities of dangerous pollutants into the air, including carbon dioxide and carbon monoxide, nitrous oxide and methane as well as hydrocarbons, nitrogen oxides and lead.

The many hours of sunshine in the Mediterranean region and the volume of pollution from vehicle exhausts, especially in summer, lead to high concentrations of the hazardous agent ozone forming in the lowest level of the atmosphere. In the upper atmosphere ozone acts as a shield against ultraviolet radiation, but it is toxic and at street level causes respiratory problems, headaches and eye irritation. And it is a greenhouse gas.

Nor is acid rain alien to the Mediterranean. This phenomenon, caused mainly by sulphur dioxide and nitrogen oxides from coal- and oil-burning power stations and from cars, is associated in most people's minds with northern Europe. Various studies, however, have shown that dry, acidic deposits also damage vegetation and buildings around the Mediterranean, among them such historic monuments as the Parthenon and the pyramids.

Several Mediterranean countries also play a leading role in another air pollution problem: the destruction of the ozone layer. Israel, Greece, Italy Spain and France all produce ozone-destroying chemicals such as chloro-fluorocarbons (CFCs), which are uncontrollably changing the structure of the upper atmosphere. The long-term consequences are unknown. Less ozone in the upper atmosphere means more harmful radiation from the sun reaching ground level. Among the projected effects are damage to life in the oceans, reduced crop yields and various threats to human health.

Urban air pollution, acid rain, ozone depletion and global warming are all unexpected symptoms of a practice that must be brought to an end: using the atmosphere as a dumping ground.

What causes the greenhouse effect?

The natural greenhouse effect makes our planet habitable: gases such as carbon dioxide in the atmosphere act as a blanket and stop some of the heat from the sun escaping back into space. But, since the beginning of the industrial revolution, increasing quantities of the greenhouse gases have been discharged into the atmosphere. The amount is now measured in billions of tonnes each year. If emissions continue to grow at the present rate, the average surface temperature of the Earth may be 1°C warmer by 2030 and around 3°C warmer by the end of the next century. Never before will the Earth have undergone such a large change in temperature in so short a time. In the 10,000 years since the end of the last ice age the temperature has risen by only 4 or 5°C. The gases that are adding to the greenhouse effect are:

Carbon dioxide (CO_2). Carbon dioxide is the most abundant greenhouse gas and is responsible for about half of current global warming. Its concentration in the atmosphere has risen by 25 percent since the late 18th century and is now increasing at the rate of 0.4 percent per year. Detailed measurements since 1958 show a rise from 315 to 350 parts per million. The primary sources of carbon dioxide are the burning of fossil fuels – coal, oil and gas – and deforestation, particularly the cutting down and burning of rainforests.

Methane (CH_4). Methane is responsible for 18 percent of global warming. Concentrations in the atmosphere are rising fast, at the rate of 1 percent per year. Each molecule of methane has about 20 times more impact on warming than a molecule of carbon dioxide.

Methane is produced by bacteria in water-logged soils – swamps, marshes and rice paddies – and in the digestive systems of ruminants such as cattle. Leaks from natural gas pipelines and emissions from landfill sites also add to

Acid drops
Evergreen trees are particularly susceptible to the effects of air pollution because they keep most of their leaves all through the year. Increasing soil acidity may also contribute to their eventual decline.

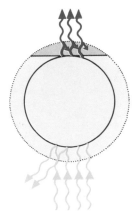

The greenhouse effect
Radiation from the sun penetrates the atmosphere and warms the surface of the planet. The Earth emits this energy as infra-red radiation, but some is trapped by certain gases in the atmosphere, so keeping the Earth at a habitable temperature. This is the natural 'greenhouse effect'. But these gases are building up in the atmosphere, enhancing the greenhouse effect and warming up the Earth.

The receding shore
A sandy beach in northern Sinai, Egypt, showing signs of severe erosion. Rising sea level will only accelerate the retreat of the soft, low-lying shores that make up nearly half of the Mediterranean coastline.

the amount of methane in the atmosphere. There is little definitive knowledge about which sources release the most methane, but the rapid rise in levels may also be the result of changes in the chemical composition of the lower atmosphere – again as a result of human activities – allowing methane to remain in the atmosphere for a longer period of time.

Even so, compared to the other greenhouse gases, methane has a short life in the atmosphere and this has led scientists to estimate that concentrations could be stabilized at present levels if emissions were cut by between 10 and 20 percent. This could be done by finding alternative methods of growing rice; improving the management of livestock; and encouraging people to eat less meat, so fewer cattle would be needed in the first place.

Nitrous oxide (N_2O). The concentration of nitrous oxide has increased by between 5 and 10 percent since the industrial revolution began, and is rising by about 0.8 percent a year. The cause of this rise is uncertain although nitrogen-based fertilizers are an important factor. As a greenhouse gas, nitrous oxide is 200 times more powerful per molecule than carbon dioxide.

Chlorofluorocarbons (CFCs). As well as destroying the ozone layer, CFCs are potent greenhouse gases. Estimates of their contribution to global warming vary between 17 and 24 percent. CFCs have an impact on warming 20,000 times greater per molecule than carbon dioxide, and their concentration is increasing rapidly – at more than 4 percent annually since 1974. CFCs are used in a wide range of products, including air-conditioning units and refrigerators, foam plastics, aerosols and solvents. Although the production of CFCs is now slowly being phased out – after overwhelming evidence came in 1986 of the damage they do to the ozone layer – the chemicals that are replacing them also contribute to the greenhouse effect.

THE GREENHOUSE EFFECT IN THE MEDITERRANEAN

The Mediterranean is the only ocean that has given its name to a precisely defined climate, characterized by hot, dry summers and mild, damp winters. Global warming would have a very great impact here, both in the changes it would bring to rainfall and in other ways such as a rise in sea level.

The Nile under threat
The Nile delta, shown (right) in a composite satellite image, is vital to the Egyptian economy. Besides rich coastal fishing grounds, it contains virtually all of Egypt's farmland (shown in red in the photograph). Nearly 50 percent of the population make their home there. According to models devised by UNEP, a rise in sea level of 1 metre or more (including land subsidence) could inundate low-lying land within 30 kilometres of the coast, affecting millions of people and about 15 percent of Egypt's cultivated land. Some coastal barriers already exist, but the cost of providing additional protection – and remedying the damaging effects of the rising sea – could be crippling.

Although it is difficult to forecast exactly how the pattern of rainfall will change in the Mediterranean, various authors agree that it will be of notable proportions in the next 40 to 70 years. Broadly speaking, we can expect higher rainfall in the north, but less in the south; hotter, drier summers will be more frequent, as will droughts, torrential rains and storms at sea.

Changes in other weather systems would influence the Mediterranean basin, too: the Asian monsoon, for example, could shift westwards, penetrating the eastern Mediterranean and bringing with it much more rain to swell the waters of the Nile.

In the autumn of 1990, the IPCC concluded that if the Earth does warm as expected in the next few decades, the expanding oceans and water from melting glaciers and the Greenland ice sheet will produce a rise in sea level of 20 centimetres by 2030, and of 65 centimetres by the end of the next century. In the Mediterranean, subsidence in some coastal areas could result in the sea level effectively rising five times higher than this.

The change in rainfall pattern and the rise of marine waters will have a forceful impact on the Mediterranean environment and its people. In coastal zones, beaches may be eroded; coastal plains, deltas and islands could be flooded – some permanently; tides may penetrate river estuaries; ports, towns, buildings and roads could be damaged. Some natural coves, rich in marine life, could disappear as the sea spreads inland.

The heat is on
A coal-fired power station in Greece adds its load to the atmosphere. It is time for all nations to reduce their dependence on fossil fuels, drawing instead on 'renewable' sources of energy that do not produce greenhouse gases. Most importantly, governments must offer incentives – to both manufacturers and consumers – to use energy more efficiently.

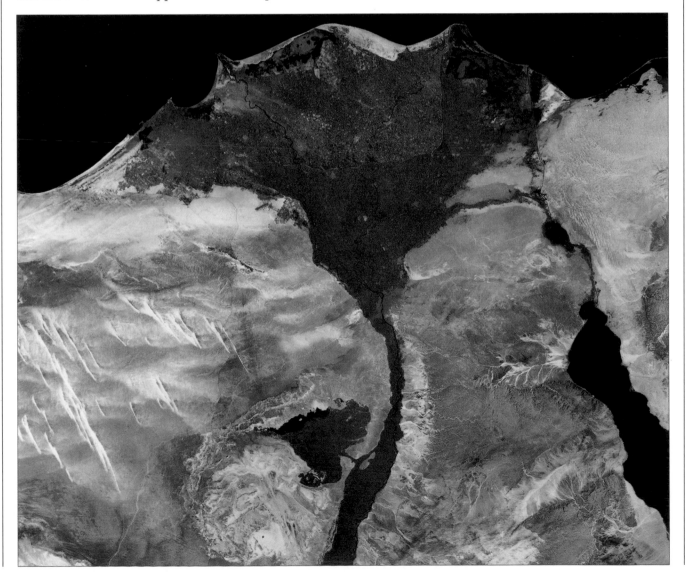

Drawing water
Fresh water is already in short supply in many parts of the Mediterranean (above), and the shortage is likely to become worse as temperatures rise and rainfall becomes ever more unpredictable.

Impoverished lands
Workers in Morocco cover bare sand dunes with branches in an attempt to halt erosion (right). Much of the soil in the Mediterranean region is impoverished (below: a micrograph of soil from Spain reveals large pockets of air beneath the surface). As the temperature rises and periods without rainfall grow longer, many cultivated lands will become increasingly arid.

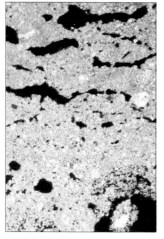

A rise in sea level of 50 centimetres or more would have catastrophic consequences, at least locally. It would simply be too expensive to construct physical barriers in all areas at risk from flooding, and politicians would have to choose which land – and therefore which communities, which people – to protect and which to leave in the hands of fate.

Fresh water is already scarce in many parts of the Mediterranean; the region's aquifers are overexploited and many are contaminated with salt water. As the sea rises, this salinization will become worse and, together with reduced rainfall, could lead to fresh water reserves being diminished by as much as 60 percent.

Nor can it be ignored that at present more than 133 million people are living in the Mediterranean coastal zone. By the year 2025 this figure could increase to 200–220 million. With such a concentration of people facing a shortage of drinking water, and their homes and livelihoods threatened, new regional conflict would seem to be inevitable.

A displacement of present agricultural zones; an increase in forest fires; changes in the ecology of the sea itself due to rising water temperature – all these are further potential consequences of our changing climate.

AN URGENT NEED FOR ACTION

The search for solutions to the rise in the greenhouse effect cannot be solely regional. A scientific study (commissioned by Greenpeace) investigated one possible course of action during the 1990s to make progress towards halting global warming:

- The urgent and complete cessation of production and consumption of CFCs and of all related chemicals that destroy the ozone layer, and avoidance of substitutes that are greenhouse gases.
- A halt to the destruction of forests, particularly tropical forests.
- A 30 percent reduction in the present level of carbon dioxide emissions.

These actions alone will not halt global warming. A programme of further cuts in carbon dioxide emissions throughout the world needs to achieve a reduction of around 70 percent by 2020. Substantial replanting of forests would also be required. There must be action taken, too, to slow the annual rise in emissions of both methane and nitrous oxide.

To be sure that we achieve these reductions in emissions, radical changes of policy will be necessary in areas as varied as transport, industry, agriculture and electricity production. Measures are needed to improve energy efficiency in all sectors of the economy; to promote public rather than private transport and the use of fuel-efficient vehicles; to develop new methods of wetland agriculture and of livestock farming.

It is vital that the world's industrialized nations, whose emissions contribute most to the problem, take the lead in cutting greenhouse gases and in preventing the waste of energy. They already have energy conservation and efficiency technologies: progressively diminishing the demand for energy is the most rapid method of reducing emissions of greenhouse gases. They need, too, to make their technology available, at affordable prices, to the less-industrialized countries, who presently fear that the measures being suggested will be too costly and act as a brake on their own economic development. These nations, in turn, must recognize that adopting coherent policies to save energy and safeguard the environment will encourage real, sustained development of natural resources without economic disadvantage.

For all nations of the Mediterranean region there are extraordinary possibilities for developing renewable sources of energy, especially solar energy. Until now, little time or money has been invested in researching their potential. Instead, resources have been directed towards the promotion of nuclear power as a means of producing electricity. Nuclear power will not stop global warming, as we discuss on pages 70–71, whereas developing the use of renewable resources will go a very long way towards it.

The magnitude of climatic changes that will result from global warming and their impact on the Mediterranean in particular makes urgently necessary a change in environmental policy, especially in coastal regions. The causes of global warming are known. The solutions to it are plain for all to see. There are no arguments whatsoever to justify inaction.

Scorching the earth
Fire rages through a forest in southwest France. Every year about 200,000 hectares of the Mediterranean basin are damaged by fire, and the threat is likely to grow as the climate changes. Fire can result in severe soil erosion as it reduces the amount of organic matter in the surface layer and, when rain does fall, nutrients in the soil will be washed away.

COUNTRY FILES

ISRAEL
Medinat Yisrael
State of Israel

AREA 20,700 sq km (excludes 7,500 sq km of the occupied territories of East Jerusalem, Gaza Strip, Golan Heights and the West Bank). **LENGTH OF COAST** 200 km. **POPULATION** 4,600,000.

Israel is a parliamentary democracy. Elections are by proportional representation; the President is head of state, while a Prime Minister and Cabinet form the government.

THE PEOPLE
Roughly 80% of the population is Jewish, and 17% Arab. A further 1,450,000 Arabs live in territories occupied by Israel. Small Druze and Bedouin communities exist. Hebrew and Arabic are both official languages. About 90% of Israelis live in towns along the coast. The official capital (not recognized by the United Nations) is Jerusalem; but most countries maintain embassies in Tel Aviv, the capital until 1967.

THE ECONOMY
LABOUR FORCE 6% in agriculture, 25% in industry, 12% in trade, 16% in financial services, 28% in government and community services.
MAJOR EXPORTS Polished diamonds, military equipment, electronics, fruit, textiles, fertilizers and chemicals.
MAJOR IMPORTS Rough diamonds, chemicals, oil, machinery, iron and steel, cereals, textiles, vehicles, ships, military equipment.
MINERAL RESOURCES Potash, copper, phosphates.
CHIEF CROPS Citrus and other fruit, vegetables.
VEHICLES 140,000 commercial, 696,000 cars.

THE ENVIRONMENT
THE PRESENT Israel has seven protected areas on coasts and rivers. There is considerable expertise in solar power, but national policy is to develop nuclear power: there is one research reactor and a reprocessing plant, waste from which is shipped down the Suez Canal. Israel has not signed the Nuclear Non-Proliferation Treaty and is now known to possess its own nuclear weapons. Heavy pesticide run-off from agricultural land reaches the sea. More than 80% of sewage is treated; 40% is used in agriculture. Tourism is economically important, and Israel has a highly developed coast with attendant problems.
THE FUTURE While Israel is environmentally one of the most forward-looking countries in the region, serious problems remain from oil, pesticides and the nuclear programme. Israel intends its nuclear arms to deter the kind of concerted attack the country has suffered in the past, but Israeli policy illustrates how military thinking habitually ignores environmental concerns.

LEBANON
al-Jumhouriya al-Lubnaniya
Lebanese Republic

AREA 10,400 sq km. **LENGTH OF COASTLINE** 200 km. **POPULATION** 3,340,000 (no official census since 1932).

Lebanon is a democracy. The President is both head of state and chief executive, and appoints the Prime Minister and Cabinet. The National Assembly is elected by proportional representation and has seats reserved for both Muslims and Christians.

THE PEOPLE
Lebanon's peoples are an ethnic mixture of Arabs (82%), Armenians (5%) and Palestinians (10%), whose allegiances are complicated by religion: 42% are Christian – mainly Maronite Catholics but with some Orthodox and other adherents – while of the 57% who are Muslim, roughly 1 million are Shi'ite, 500,000 are Sunni and 200,000 are Druze. Since the mid 1970s these groups have been at war with one another, a conflict confused by Syrian and Israeli intervention. Most wealthy Lebanese departed after the economy – based largely on financial services – collapsed in the mid 1980s. The government has no resources, poverty is worsening and, in the middle of 1991, a peace settlement seemed remote.

THE ECONOMY
LABOUR FORCE 17% in agriculture, 19% in industry, 56% in commerce and services.
MAJOR EXPORTS Gold, precious metals, citrus fruit, textiles, building materials, food, tobacco, wine, machinery and electrical apparatus.
MAJOR IMPORTS Gold, precious metals, fruit and vegetables, textiles, machinery and electrical equipment, iron and steel, motor vehicles.
MINERAL RESOURCE Iron.
CHIEF CROPS Fruit, cereals, potatoes, olives.
VEHICLES 21,000 commercial, 460,000 cars (1982).

THE ENVIRONMENT
THE PRESENT There is little heavy industry in Lebanon to create pollution, but agriculture – with attendant problems from fertilizers and pesticides – is increasingly critical to the impoverished country's survival. The chaotic conditions have allowed persons unknown to dump huge quantities of toxic waste on the Lebanese shoreline, and government resources are too scarce to prevent this or trace those responsible.
THE FUTURE Until the conflicts within Lebanon are resolved there is little scope for environmental action.

Pastoral scene in Syria
Sheep graze in a field bordering an industrial complex in Syria (right). Airborne pollution contaminates the soil and the sea, and gives growing cause for concern as nations like Syria seek to industrialize.

SYRIA

al-Jamhouriya al-Arabia as-Souriya
Syrian Arab Republic

AREA 185,180 sq km. **LENGTH OF COASTLINE** 200 km.
POPULATION 12,600,000.

The President is head of state and leader of the Ba'ath
Party, 'the leading party in the state and society',
although other political parties may stand for election.

THE PEOPLE

Nearly 90% of Syria's population is Arabic-speaking
and Muslim; Kurds (9%) and Armenians make up the
remainder. At least half the population lives in cities –
the largest are Damascus (pop. 1.36 million), Aleppo
(1.31 million) and Homs (464,000). Now growing at
4% per annum, the population will double by 2006.

THE ECONOMY

LABOUR FORCE 32% in agriculture, forestry and fishing;
29% in industry; 39% in services.
MAJOR EXPORTS Petroleum (about 50% of all exports by
value), textiles, tobacco, fruit and vegetables, cotton.
MAJOR IMPORTS Food, mineral and petroleum products,
textiles, machinery, chemicals, fertilizers.
MINERAL RESOURCES Oil (reserves: 1.4 billion barrels),
natural gas, chrome, manganese, iron, phosphates.
CHIEF CROPS Cotton, fruit, vegetables, wheat, olives.
VEHICLES 127,000 commercial, 112,000 cars.

THE ENVIRONMENT

THE PRESENT Phosphates are economically important,
and oil refineries have been built at Baniyas (on the
coast) and Homs (on the river Orontes). Pollution
from these, although not recently monitored, is likely
to be high. Fertilizers are a major import, and widely
used; as long as agriculture is the largest factor in
the GDP (over 20%), they will contribute to pollution
of the sea.
THE FUTURE A high rate of population growth and the
vagaries and inefficiency of agricultural production will
continue to pose major problems both for the Syrian
economy and for the Mediterranean environment.

TURKEY

Türkiye Cumhuriyeti
Republic of Turkey

AREA 779,452 sq km (includes 23,764 sq km in Europe).
MEDITERRANEAN COAST 5,200 km. **POPULATION** 56,700,000.

Turkey is a parliamentary democracy. The President is
head of state, elected by the Grand National Assembly,
whose majority party forms a government headed by a
Prime Minister.

THE PEOPLE

Turkish-speakers make up almost 95% of the
population; the rest mostly speak Kurdish, with a tiny
minority in the south east speaking Arabic. Some 99%
of Turks are Muslim. Since 1928 Turkey has had no
official state religion; it is illegal to use religion for
political purposes. Over 55% of the people live in
cities: the largest are Istanbul (pop. 6 million), Ankara,
the capital (4 million) and Izmir (2.5 million).

THE ECONOMY

LABOUR FORCE 56% in agriculture and fisheries; 14% in
industry; 12% in services.
MAJOR EXPORTS Cotton, tobacco, fruit, livestock,
minerals, textiles, glass, cement.
MAJOR IMPORTS Machinery, crude oil, iron and steel,
medicines and dyes, chemicals, fertilizers.
MINERAL RESOURCES Coal, oil, phosphates, iron ore,
copper, boron.
CHIEF CROPS Cereals, sugar, grapes, oranges, tea.
VEHICLES 553,000 commercial, 1.1 million cars.

THE ENVIRONMENT

THE PRESENT Industrial pollution is particularly marked
at Izmir, Iskenderun and the Sea of Marmara. Untreated
effluent pours into rivers and streams to the sea. Turkey
plans to develop nuclear power, and to build additional
coal-fired power stations (one, using highly sulphurous
lignite, in a protected area, remains incomplete after
public protests). Turkey is developing geothermal
power and is rich in hydro-electric power. The monk
seal population is probably the largest in the region,
but breeding caves have been disturbed by tourists.
Turtle nesting beaches are also threatened by tourist
developments. Turkey has a dedicated environmental
department, and a newly formed Green Party.
Environmental legislation is up to EC standards but
enforcement is poor. There are three national parks.
THE FUTURE Turkey's Mediterranean coast is largely
unspoiled, but the country is encouraging both tourism
and industrial development. The shoreline thus faces a
bleak future unless standards of cleanliness are
drastically improved and development carefully planned
– both unlikely in view of Turkey's belief that rapid
economic expansion is vital. If oil worth exploiting is
found under the Aegean, worse problems may arise –
both environmentally and in exacerbating the long-
standing dispute with Greece over mineral rights there.

THE LEVANTINE STATES

The eastern Mediterranean countries are a study in diversity – from Israel's highly fertile, sub-tropical coastal plain to the aridity of the Syrian desert.

Israel, unlike most other Mediterranean states, is essentially flat; apart from the extreme north of the country, the only substantial upland region is the occupied West Bank. More than a fifth of the land is farmed, and the upland plateau of the Negev desert in the south is now being artificially irrigated.

Lebanon is dominated by the Mount Lebanon and Anti-Lebanon ranges, which run north and south through the country. Between them lies the Bekaa valley, watered by the Litani, the country's major river, and home of most of Lebanon's agriculture. Over four fifths of the population live on the coast, however.

In Syria, the Ansariya mountains parallel the narrow coastal plain. This has heavy winter rains, but the interior, in the lee of the mountains, is arid, with very hot summers. More than half of Syria is desert.

Turkey is divided by the straits that link the Black and Mediterranean seas. High rainfall on the coast supports intensive cultivation. The south east is treeless and criss-crossed by mountains that reach right to the sea's edge. Precious mixed woodlands lie between the Anatolian plateau and the littoral plain, but these are so degraded that, unless they are protected they may disappear within 25 years.

Artisans of the sea
Boats on the Syrian island of Arwad (above), off Tartous, attest to the survival of the fishing industry – despite Syria's own oil-refining industry, which is based at sites nearby and affects local fishing grounds. On the mainland, the coast is relatively short, intensively cultivated and densely populated.

Natural disappearance
The coast at Dor between Haifa and Tel Aviv in Israel (left) is eroding naturally, as wave action eats into the soft, sandy soil. Israel is a relative oddity among Mediterranean countries in having a consistently sandy coast with low-lying cliffs, rather than the steep, rocky shores typical of much of the region.

The garden of Lebanon
The Bekaa valley (below) nestles between Lebanon's two great mountain ranges. Protected on all sides from extremes of weather, the valley is intensively farmed. Since civil war divided the country in the mid 1970s, agriculture has become increasingly important in Lebanon.

Turtles before tourists
Dalyan beach in Turkey (left) is one of the region's few nesting sites for loggerhead turtles (Caretta caretta, above). While plans for a huge tourist complex here have been shelved, and the site is now protected, restrictions on the use of the beach are poorly enforced.

FISHING
THE PLUNDER OF THE SEA

THE MILLION TONNES or so of fish that are taken each year from the Mediterranean make up a mere 1.2 percent of the world catch. Yet this relatively small quantity, destined almost entirely for human consumption, is worth between 5 and 6 percent of the world market. Mediterranean fish, in other words, fetch high prices.

Fish are relatively scarce in the Mediterranean because the sea is not as fertile as others. Most marine life flourishes in the food-rich waters of the continental shelf, but in many Mediterranean areas this is very narrow: shallow coastal water plunges rapidly, in some places, to more than 2,000 metres. In addition, the sea is fed by just a few large rivers, which naturally discharge comparatively few nutrients. (The recent massive increase in nutrients from human sources has not resulted in more fish, because the Mediterranean ecosystem has evolved with low nutrient levels.) The distinct separation of the warmer surface waters from the colder layers below means that once nutrients have sunk into the deeper water, they are not available again to the life in the upper layers – except in a few areas where rising currents do bring them back to the surface.

About 100 species are fished commercially in the Mediterranean. Of the fish in the surface and mid (pelagic) waters, pilchard and anchovy are the main species, and mackerel, horse mackerel, tuna, swordfish and gilthead

Fishing to live
Many individuals still subsist by fishing, but it is increasingly a commercial enterprise.

An end to the driftnet?
Driftnets, which capture and kill virtually all creatures that swim into them, are now banned in Italy and Spain.

The modern tradition
Fishermen tending their nets off the coast of the Peloponnese in Greece. Even small, traditional boats may be fitted with powerful engines and sophisticated equipment such as echo-location devices.

sea-bream are also important. Closer to the bottom, a large number of different species are sought, including red mullet, hake, whiting, blue whiting, common sole and sea bass, as well as shrimps and octopus.

Assessing the stocks

In an attempt to ascertain the amount of fishing that the Mediterranean can support, scientists have analysed about a quarter of the 110 populations in the waters of Spain, France, Italy and Greece, the Mediterranean states belonging to the EC (with Tunisia, these four account for 70 percent of the Mediterranean catch). By analysing the number of eggs and young fish and the fish actually caught, it is possible to calculate, roughly, how many fish there are in the sea and how many can be taken in future without depleting the stocks.

But the information on which the statistics are based is often very poor, as many scientists themselves admit; and various, contentious, methods of analysis are used. It is almost impossible to gauge accurately how many fish are taken from the Mediterranean each year, because the fishermen land their catches at a very large number of sites around the coast, frequently without any records being made. The total catch from the Mediterranean is probably underestimated by between 20 and 30 percent, and in some countries the true catch could be twice as big as is declared. In some cases, estimates of population levels differ by as much as eightfold for the same stocks.

As a result, different institutions issue wildly differing statistics; for example, scientists estimated that the total weight of fish landed in 1989 in Italy (the country that makes the largest catch in the Mediterranean) was 800,000 tonnes – but the very same figure is used in other reports for the total catch that year made by all the Mediterranean coastal states.

In general, fisheries authorities consider that stocks of bottom-dwelling or demersal fish are already fished to the limit and that some are overexploited, to the point where the population of certain species may be in danger of collapse. Some pelagic stocks may also be overfished.

DIFFERENT FISHING METHODS

Practically all fishing techniques known throughout the world, from the most rudimentary to the highly sophisticated, are practised in the Mediterranean

A massive catch
Such quantities of fish have been taken from the sea in the past that the populations of certain species are in danger of collapse.

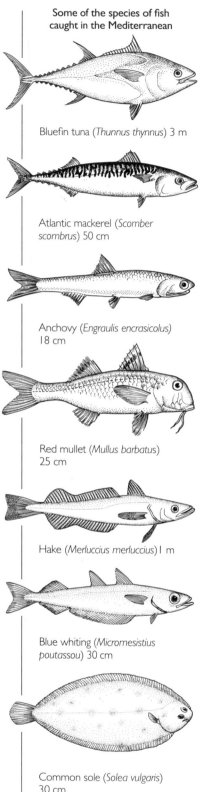

Some of the species of fish caught in the Mediterranean

Bluefin tuna (*Thunnus thynnus*) 3 m

Atlantic mackerel (*Scomber scombrus*) 50 cm

Anchovy (*Engraulis encrasicolus*) 18 cm

Red mullet (*Mullus barbatus*) 25 cm

Hake (*Merluccius merluccius*) 1 m

Blue whiting (*Micromesistius poutassou*) 30 cm

Common sole (*Solea vulgaris*) 30 cm

region, and in some areas subsistence and commercial fishing exist together. The 'artisanal' or small-scale fishing sector uses the greatest variety of gear including, just to name a few: fixed (or set) and drifting gill nets, entangling nets, traps, lines, longlines and small seines. Such a wide range of gear enables all kinds of habitat to be exploited, spreading the fishing effort over a large number of species. This fleet, which in some countries accounts for up to 90 percent of the whole, fishes mainly on demersal species, supplying high-quality products to the fresh seafood market.

However, the bulk of the catch from Mediterranean waters is landed by purse seiners, fishing on both small and large pelagic species; by trawlers, which fish on demersal stocks and/or small pelagic species; and, to a lesser extent, by longlines, driftnets and various kinds of trap, catching mostly tunids and other large pelagic species such as swordfish.

Types of fishing gear

Purse seines account for the largest part of the catch in the Mediterranean. They are designed to capture shoals of fish, attracted to the nets by the lights often used with them. Once the shoal is surrounded, the bottom of the net is closed, preventing escape. Purse seining is potentially highly selective, and can be used to target specific shoals; but it is very damaging to fish stocks when the net is intentionally set on juvenile shoals, of tuna for example.

The traditional bottom trawler in the Mediterranean uses a bag-like net with an opening as wide as 20 metres and about 2 metres high. The net is kept open by a pair of 'kites' or 'otter boards', which are pushed far apart by the pressure of the water flowing against them, and by floats attached to the top of the net mouth and tens of kilograms of chains at the bottom. The boat tows the net for several hours at a time over a distance of about 15 kilometres or more. Each trawl may sweep more than 100,000 square metres of seabed, in the process catching or disrupting all life to be found there.

Many juvenile fish are caught by this method, although the number could be reduced if the Mediterranean countries adopted – and put into effect – the larger mesh size (20 millimetres square) recommended by the General Fisheries Council for the Mediterranean (GFCM), a regional body established by the UN's Food and Agriculture Organization (FAO). Some countries have set 20 millimetres square as the compulsory mesh size for trawlers, but no one takes care to ensure that the law is enforced.

A fast-growing problem in the Mediterranean is caused by so-called 'pelagic trawls', fishing gear that allows trawlers to fish in mid water as well as on the sea bottom. The boats operating this gear use much more powerful engines than other trawlers; they tow a net with a much smaller mesh size than the legal limit for bottom trawlers and whose mouth ranges from 10 to 15 metres in height. A pelagic trawler captures anything – adults and juveniles alike – that may be in its path, from the bottom reaches (when used, inappropriately, in shallow water) to mid water. There are strong suspicions, too, that dolphins may be trapped by this new gear.

Furthermore, the net is dragged at a relatively high speed, and the flow of water over the threads of the already small mesh (9-12 millimetres square) creates a pressure wave, a physical barrier that reduces the opening of the mesh even further, so that many more, smaller, fish are also caught.

Another technique favoured throughout the Mediterranean basin is the longline: a 'mother' line, often several kilometres long, to which thousands of shorter and thinner lines are tied every few metres and to which, in turn, hooks are attached. Floats and weights help to keep the gear at the surface or at the required depth. Target species are swordfish, tunids, sharks and, using

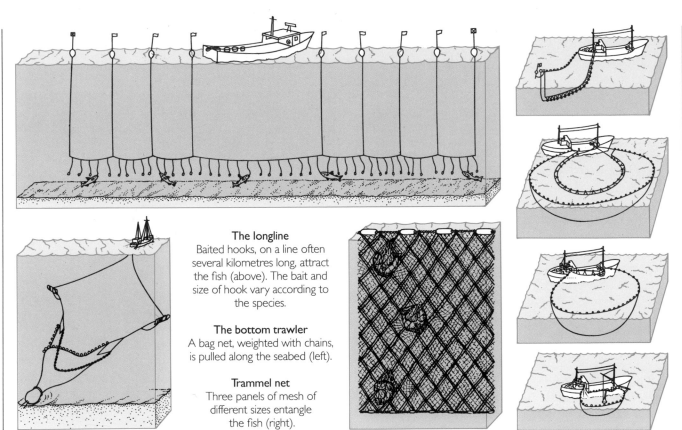

The longline
Baited hooks, on a line often several kilometres long, attract the fish (above). The bait and size of hook vary according to the species.

The bottom trawler
A bag net, weighted with chains, is pulled along the seabed (left).

Trammel net
Three panels of mesh of different sizes entangle the fish (right).

much smaller hooks and different bait, demersal species. Surface longlines are a serious hazard to sea turtles: tens of thousands are estimated to be caught by these each year. This could be reduced if fishermen avoided the turtles' foraging grounds, used larger hooks and bait, or fished at greater depths.

A multitude of other techniques is also used by the artisanal fleet in the Mediterranean, helping to distribute the fishing effort so that no one species is under intensive pressure. The bulk of gear is made up of fixed (or set) nets of different design. Most notorious of these are trammel nets, usually up to 2.5 metres high and formed by two large-mesh (200 millimetre) panels sandwiching a looser and smaller-mesh panel (30-40 millimetres). The fish that swim through them get tangled up in the three layers of net.

Driftnetting is a particularly indiscriminate technique. The net or group of nets is usually several kilometres in length and up to 30 metres deep and it simply hangs in the water. The size of the mesh does vary according to the target species, which are mostly swordfish or albacore and bonitos, but the nets threaten many other fish, as well as dolphins, whales, turtles and birds.

The purse seine
A long net is set out around a shoal of fish and the bottom drawn up, as if with a purse string, to contain them.

The driftnet
A wall of netting is set out across an area where fish are known to swim — on the bottom, in mid water, or at the surface.

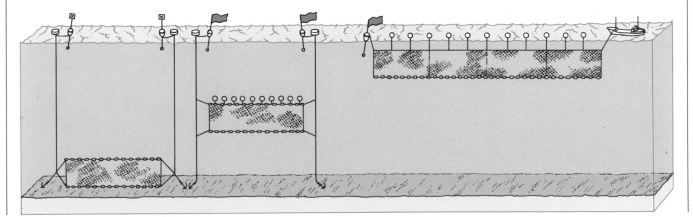

AQUACULTURE

Aquaculture, mostly oyster, mussel and fish culture in brackish water, is traditional in the Mediterranean. In naturally sheltered areas such as the Venice lagoons, fish culture has taken place for centuries. But, over the years, the habitats have been increasingly controlled in order to rear the highest number of fish possible.

Today, aquaculture is carried out in almost all of the Mediterranean countries and plays a major role in the supply of seafood in the region. The huge resources dedicated to its development resulted in an estimated total production of 530,000 tonnes in 1986.

The northern countries, especially France, Italy and Spain, have a good deal of expertise in aquaculture, but competition for space on this highly developed coastline is fierce, as is the competition for customers between those people who catch fish and those who farm them. Elsewhere, however, there are still huge resources, both of potential sites and of wild fish fry and juvenile shellfish that can be brought in for rearing.

A drawback to fish farming in the Mediterranean is that in many countries the fish are carnivorous species, fed on high-protein pellets that, in terms of the environment, are costly to produce. In addition, the nutrient-laden waste from the fish pens contaminates the surrounding sea, contributing to eutrophication and oxygen depletion, particularly in sheltered and enclosed areas. However, some states, such as Egypt, concentrate on vegetarian species and those that feed on detritus – grey mullet for example – and these have far less impact on the environment.

Suspended animation
The Mediterranean's gentle tides are particularly favourable to mussel cultivation (above). Mussel 'seedlings' are suspended in the sea on ropes hung from poles or large floats.

Close quarters
Sea bass (left) are now farmed intensively in floating cages near the coast – although the technique of keeping fish larvae alive caused some difficulties in the early stages of modern aquaculture. Today, fry reared in hatcheries are held in enclosures and fed with fishmeal pellets or minced fish until they reach a marketable size. Waste waters, polluted with nutrients, are released directly into the sea.

Foreign fleets in the Mediterranean

The majority of the Mediterranean fleet is owned by the fishermen themselves or by individual shipowners, since large companies have not yet penetrated this side of the industry. But foreign industrial fleets do exploit the Mediterranean's international waters, and there are no exclusive economic zones (EEZs), which extend the rights of the coastal states beyond their territorial waters, as there are in other seas. Asian industrial fleets, for example, enter the Mediterranean in late spring to fish for spawning bluefin tuna, a species already heavily exploited, mostly in the waters surrounding the Balearic islands, but also in the straits of Sicily and off Libyan waters.

The Mediterranean states have instituted no international convention for the exploitation of living marine resources, so they have no control over what foreign fleets do. The number of these vessels operating in Mediterranean waters, and the times of year when they can fish, are regulated by the legislation, if any, in each fleet's own country.

The problem is worsened by other vessels that operate under 'flags of convenience': they take fish from the sea without providing any details of the catch – species, size or age – or any of the other information required to draw up policies to manage and conserve marine resources.

EFFECTS OF OVERFISHING

When a species is fished heavily, the effects can be felt throughout the ecosystem – with consequences that cannot be predicted. The population of the species may be so reduced that it is incapable of recovering to its former level and its ecological niche may then be filled by another species. This may have been one of the factors responsible for the recent replacement of the pilchard by the anchovy in the waters of southeastern Spain and of Morocco.

It is not only the target species that are affected by the fishing industry. Other fish and marine creatures are often caught in the nets or on the lines (when they are known as a by-catch). Both the biological and the physical

Tuna trapping
Sicilian fishermen use a gigantic, trap (below) to capture shoals of tuna as they migrate from the Atlantic to spawning grounds in the Mediterranean. Thrashing around in the water, the fish quickly become so exhausted that the fishermen can spike them and then haul them on board (above). Tuna have been so intensively fished that their stocks are becoming depleted. A particular threat comes from the growing numbers of Asian longliners, which take huge quantities of tuna without reference to any authority in the Mediterranean.

A structure for life
Artificial reefs on the seabed discourage trawlers from working illegally in shallow, coastal waters because of the danger that the fishing nets will become snagged and therefore unusable. The reefs also provide a haven for many kinds of fish and other marine creatures, which feed in and around them and use them as spawning grounds.

environment often suffer too, particularly in the coastal shelf areas. It is here that the meadows of the plant *Posidonia* flourish, providing shelter for a diverse range of marine life. But bottom trawling – though forbidden in such shallow, coastal water – is helping to destroy this precious ecosystem, the fishing gear ripping up the meadows as it is dragged along the seabed.

Other consequences of intensive fishing are less visible. For example, small pelagic species that are usually eaten by other fish, marine mammals, birds and reptiles are taken as by-catches, so reducing their predators' food supply. It is very difficult to assess what the effects of this loss are.

Dolphins are threatened by fishing in a different way. Some are deliberately harpooned, and their flesh used as bait for the shrimp fishery. And increasing numbers are being killed by fishermen because of the fish they eat from the nets and the damage they allegedly cause to the gear in the process. The problem is not new in the Mediterranean, but it does seem to be growing – possibly because it is becoming harder for dolphins to find their prey in the open water, or because they are being opportunistic in catching their food.

REGULATIONS

All Mediterranean states have issued their own regulations to manage the fishing industry and control the amount of fishing that takes place in the sea. But, in countries such as Spain, for example, many of the laws are issued or modified by the regional governments, and are looser and weaker – from an environmental point of view – than the national legislation, because the politicians in the communities concerned are under more immediate social pressure. The result is a chaotic and cumbersome set of laws, poorly enforced because they have low political priority and consequently broken with impunity by fishermen.

The introduction of closed seasons has brought some positive results, allowing, for example, more young fish to survive to become breeding

POSIDONIA

The plant and animal life of the Mediterranean is richest near the coast. Sunlight can reach the bottom of these relatively shallow waters, so that plant life thrives. The plants provide food, a haven for breeding and a habitat for a huge variety of creatures, large and small, which in turn feed on one another.

The marine plant *Posidonia oceanica*, which is found only in the Mediterranean, plays a key part in this food web. *Posidonia* is not a seaweed nor an alga, but a terrestrial flowering plant that has returned to the sea. It takes root in sand and mud sometimes very close to the shore but usually at depths of between 5 and 40 metres. Here, it flowers in spring, produces fruit, and sheds its leaves in the autumn. It grows in vast meadows or prairies, forming a dense mat of leaves, detritus, roots and silt that absorbs the energy of the waves and helps to protect the coast from erosion.

Posidonia, like all plants, generates oxygen through photosynthesis. A single square metre of leaves produces 10 litres of oxygen a day, so that a meadow provides a plentiful supply of oxygen as well as food and shelter for thousands of species of bacteria, algae, plankton, crustaceans and newly hatched fish.

Any threat to *Posidonia* will have considerable knock-on effects through the food web. And *Posidonia* prairies are shrinking all over the Mediterranean, poisoned by pollution, deprived of light by mud dumped from dredgers and silt created by stripping the land of vegetation for building projects, and ripped out by trawlers fishing illegally in shallow coastal waters. But the trawlermen are only helping to destroy their own livelihood. Without the *Posidonia* meadows and the food, shelter and oxygen they supply, fish stocks will, inevitably, decline and change.

Life-giving prairies
Wrasse are just one of thousands of species that live among beds of *Posidonia oceanica* (right) in the coastal waters of the Mediterranean. Besides providing food and shelter, the sea grass is also an important source of oxygen and organic material. But this essential ecosystem is disappearing: not only killed by pollution and destroyed by trawling, it is also smothered by silt and mud dumped during construction works on the shore (below) .

Beach balls
Thousands of seagrass balls line a Mediterranean beach (right). The fibrous tissue around the base of the *Posidonia* plant often washes up on the shore, where the wind and the waves mould it into these soft rounded shapes.

Back to the sea
Such is the demand for Mediterranean fish that the fleet cannot keep pace with it. But only certain kinds of fish fetch the high prices the big trawlers need to meet their operating costs, and a large part of the catch – which is, of course, now dead – is simply thrown overboard. Only seabirds can benefit from this wasteful practice.

adults. But the whole legislation, throughout the region, must be carefully reviewed and harmonized if there is to be any prospect of the fisheries being 'managed' successfully. And any such policy must go beyond national borders: the EC, for example, could provide the necessary framework when it extends its Common Fisheries Policy to cover its Mediterranean members in 1992.

FISHERIES – THE FUTURE?

There are two main trends in the Mediterranean fisheries. Overcapitalization means that too much is invested in boats and gear in relation to the long-term return on that investment that may be expected from the fish available. In order to compete successfully for an increasingly scarce resource, fisher-men buy bigger, more powerful boats, fitted with ever more sophisticated – and expensive – equipment to detect and catch the fish.

There is growing competition, too, from fleets in other waters with greater resources, which are so well equipped that they can flood the Mediterranean market with cheap fish. The market is also changing, with increased demand for pre-cooked fish products as well as high-quality fresh fish. The sales dis-tribution networks of both often bypass the local fishermen.

These trends seem certain to change the nature of Mediterranean fishing, from a traditional small-scale endeavour, using a variety of methods to suit the diversity of habitats and species, to a large-scale industrial enterprise.

Workable regulation of the fisheries, which takes a precautionary stance and both addresses and admits our limited understanding of the natural ecosystem, is now extremely urgent. Centuries ago, when there was no knowledge of such concepts as 'standing biomass' or 'maximum sustainable yield', the Mediterranean fisheries were successfully regulated by taking a conservative approach based on the effects they could see the industry was having on fish stocks, and the legislation that was issued was strictly enforced. It was only with the massive power of modern technology and the often misguided application of science that problems began.

Solutions will come, too, only when governments progress to an integrated management of the coastal belt, in which fisheries are considered in the larger context of environmental issues and human activities.

What must be remembered, however, is that no matter how good the legislation is, it will be impotent unless there is the political will to enforce it, and the people who work in the industry can be convinced that changes must be made if the fish, the fishermen and the environment are to survive.

RED CORAL

Divers have taken red coral (*Corallium rubrum*), which is almost unique to the Mediterranean, from the sea for centuries, to be carved into jewellery, coins and even talismans for use in healing. Now the coral beds have been virtually destroyed, thanks not only to new mechanical methods of stripping it from the sea bottom and its over-exploitation by scuba divers who have no regard for any regulation, but also to the destruction caused by trawl nets and their weights.

Red coral is an unusual form of ancient animal life, the simplest to have developed a nervous system. It is related to the true corals and to anemones and hydras but, unlike the latter, the individuals of the species cannot survive as distinct entities. A branch of red coral consists of many individual animals, a colony whose structure is supported by a combination of calcium carbonate and a horny material that the cells secrete. When the animals die, the calcium carbonate, coloured by pigment, remains as a stone skeleton. This is the material from which coral jewellery is carved.

Red coral once thrived all over the Mediterranean. It lives in deep, dark currents of water, between 50 and 200 metres below the surface, and even in almost lightless caves and crevices. There it attaches itself to solid rock and grows at a rate possibly as low as 2 millimetres a year, feeding on tiny crustaceans and other zooplankton. The colony's tentacles and bodies in turn provide food for fish.

Coral has traditionally been 'fished' by divers, and the rate of extraction has therefore been limited by human endurance. But the 1960s saw the invention of the 'Italian bar', a crude device consisting of a heavy beam up to 6 metres long, weighted by chains, with nets attached. Dragged along the seabed by a boat, this smashes everything in its path: it also collects as little as a fifth of the coral growths that it destroys.

Although banned in many countries, the Italian bar is still used. Trawling nets and their chains have a similar effect on the beds – yet another reason for controlling such a destructive fishing technique

Hidden treasure
A bed of red coral (*Corallium rubrum*) thrives with sponges and hydroids in the depths of the sea (above). Only about 40 tonnes of coral is reportedly taken from the Mediterranean each year, but many times that amount is killed accidentally by fishermen.

A sting in the tail
Red coral consists of hundreds of single animals linked through their skeletons and their nervous systems. Individuals can be identified by their polyps the eight-tentacled translucent tubes (left) that reach out from each animal to capture passing zooplankton. The tentacles close on the prey and sting it to death. The creature is then drawn down into the stomach and digested internally.

TOURISM
THE PRICE THE MEDITERRANEAN PAYS

THE MEDITERRANEAN is the world's favourite playground: at least one in every three people who travel abroad for their holidays goes to the Mediterranean. In 1990 some 150 million holidaymakers visited a Mediterranean country, about three quarters going to Spain, France and Italy. In the 1980s, on average, international tourists contributed 6.5 percent of the gross domestic product to the 18 Mediterranean states. In Israel, Cyprus and Malta, they contributed between 12 and 15 percent. In Morocco, tourists are the second most important source of foreign exchange.

Seasonal disturbance

Nearly two thirds of these people will have taken their holidays in the space of just four months, between June and September. In the eastern and southern countries of the region, the numbers are more evenly spread throughout the year, but as a whole tourism in the Mediterranean is markedly seasonal. This cramming of people into little space and a brief time will, according to United Nations projections, become still more intense in the future: as many as 184 million people may visit the coast alone in the year 2000, and as many as 341 million by the year 2025.

Most tourists in the Mediterranean are from central and northern Europe – with Germany in the lead, followed by the United Kingdom. The number of tourists from the USA is increasing in the southern and eastern countries. And many people in Spain, France and Italy holiday at the seaside, either within their own borders or in other Mediterranean countries.

A Mediterranean holiday means a holiday by the sea. Nearly all the 150 million visitors to the region in 1990 will have been funnelled into the sea's narrow coastal strip. The result of this huge annual influx of people has been an intense urbanization of the coast, especially in the north west. In certain parts of the French Riviera and the Spanish Costa del Sol, Costa Brava and Costa Blanca almost 90 percent of the shoreline has been filled with buildings dedicated to tourists in one way or another. Most of these buildings are hotels, but recent years have seen the development of 'self-catering' villas and apartments; second homes belonging to city dwellers are also common. In France, Malta and parts of Italy, these new developments have overtaken the hotel industry as a source of accommodation for visitors.

The attractions of the Mediterranean are well known. According to UNEP research, most tourists come in search of sun, sea and sand (especially those who visit the south and east), followed closely by those touring the ancient monuments in which the region – the cradle of civilization – abounds. But an overriding factor is economic. A Mediterranean holiday is cheap, especially in Tunisia, Yugoslavia, Spain, Italy – and Turkey, the latest of the Mediterranean countries to be 'discovered' by mass tourism.

The drawbacks to pleasure

The changes mass tourism has brought since it began in the 1960s have been radical. On the coasts, more than half the working population are now dependent in some degree on the tourist industry, while in Rhodes, the Côte d'Azur and the Balearics virtually the entire local economy rests on tourism.

Heaven and hell
The explosion of mass tourism since the 1960s has transformed Benidorm, on Spain's Costa Blanca. In the 1940s (top), this was a tranquil traditional village. The modern town (above) is a mass of anonymous high-rise hotels, where visitors consume vast quantities of water – and generate untold quantities of sewage.

Traditional ways of life and of making a living – such as agriculture, forestry, skilled labour and industry – have declined as a consequence.

In less developed societies – those in the south and east of the region especially – tourism has also introduced new values, assumptions and ways of life to the host countries. Here, traditional customs, crafts and even dress have often been reduced to tourist attractions themselves as their original significance has been lost.

And, in the process, the environment has suffered. The seasonal press of humanity has made enormous demands on the land through the spread of residential development, hotel building, sporting marinas, and road building,

The invasion of Venice
Tourists in Venice (left) crowd along a walkway built over St Mark's Square following a flood of the Venice Lagoon. Tourists make huge demands on the resources of this unique Italian city – so great that in 1987 it was closed briefly to visitors.

and in additional services such as solid and liquid waste disposal, and day-to-day trade and commerce. And because all this activity has been concentrated into a narrow coastal zone, the transformation of the landscape has been all the more severe. Both natural wilderness and agricultural land have suffered. The draining of wetlands to build facilities for tourists, the destruction of dunes and woodlands for residential development, and the massive occupation of the shoreline by huge concrete blocks or by interminable chains of small villas and chalets – all these are the visible effects of tourism on the Mediterranean coastline. As the ecological impact has been uniformly negative, so too has the beauty of the landscape been destroyed.

Demanding guests

The concentration of the permanent population and of tourists along the coast has also aggravated the problems of water supply, waste disposal and energy consumption. The height of the tourist season coincides with the period of least rainfall in the Mediterranean. This is also the time when water is in greatest demand for agriculture. Some Greek islands have to import water by tanker during the summer months to make up the shortfall, but the

problem is also acute in the Balearics, the Yugoslavian islands and Djerba, off Tunisia. In some areas such is the demand for water that the groundwater level has been reduced and salt water has infiltrated the aquifers.

Tourists also produce phenomenal quantities of waste. In a region where 85 percent of sewage is discharged untreated into the sea, this has turned many parts of the Mediterranean into a health hazard for bathers. Solid waste – household rubbish – has to be disposed of somehow. And less obvious forms of waste, such as car exhaust fumes, contribute to air pollution.

Hidden costs

The increase in population and seasonal activity along this narrow strip of territory has also led to massive extra demands on energy supplies. More power stations – themselves agents of pollution – have had to be built, while rubbish disposal and the provision of local services such as drains and roads have also led directly and indirectly to increased oil consumption, depletion of natural resources as well as further pressures on the water supply. All this is to satisfy demands that arise in just three or four months of the year; for the rest of the time they are under-used, but their maintenance remains an economic drain. Where such developments and services have not caught up with tourist demand, the existing resources are stretched to breaking point.

Many who have studied the impact of tourism on the Mediterranean have described it as 'neocolonial': in the Mediterranean, in other words, tourism is another expression of the economic and cultural power of rich nations over poor, while the tourists themselves show little or no respect for the sensibilities and culture of their hosts. This may not be true in the northwest of the region; but what is certain is that the Mediterranean coastal societies are becoming dedicated almost entirely to tourism, and what they provide is dictated by the demands of visitors from northern and central Europe. In effect, these countries control the coastal economies in the region, although local communities continue to welcome tourist development as a rapid route to affluence. Yet this relationship has involved brutal land speculation, the laundering of dubious money and a massive turnover of capital. There is every reason to believe that, if left unchecked, the underlying economics of tourism will destroy not only the ecology but the human societies of the Mediterranean littoral still further.

A fleeting idyll
Kalkan, in Turkey (above), resembles many a tourist's dream: unspoiled – and undiscovered by other tourists. But, in response, new building has already begun.

Spread the load
In summer, Varkiza beach near Athens (left) is lined with people and their cars. The stress on both humanity and the environment could be vastly reduced if people took holidays throughout the year.

The human catch
Tourists go boating on the Nile (right). In most Mediterranean states traditional occupations have given way to the profitable business of entertaining visitors.

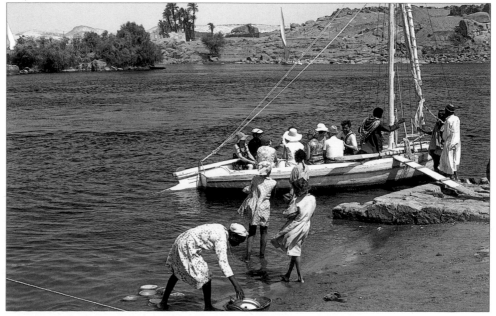

SEA TURTLES

Both the loggerhead turtle (*Caretta caretta*) and the green turtle (*Chelonia mydas*) live, feed and nest in the Mediterranean. The hawksbill (*Eretmochelys imbricata*) and leatherback (*Dermochelys coriacea*) enter the sea sporadically from the Atlantic, and the Kemp's Ridley (*Lepidochelys kempi*) is suspected to do so: all are sighted most often in the area of the Gibraltar Strait.

Some 2,000 female loggerhead turtles nest on the northeastern coast each year, mostly on the beaches of Greece and Turkey and particularly in the Bay of Laganas in Zakynthos and at Dalyan. Only a few small groups, no more than a hundred individuals, nest in other eastern and southern Mediterranean countries. Between 300 and 1,000 green turtles appear to congregate on the beaches of Cyprus and Turkey. It has been suggested that leatherbacks nest in some Mediterranean areas, but there is no evidence of this.

The greatest threat to the survival of Mediterranean sea turtles is to be found at the place where their lives begin: the beach. The tourists' constant search for new, clean beaches, away from the degraded shores of the western Mediterranean, has now spread to such countries as Turkey, Greece and Cyprus. Here, large coastal areas once used by turtles as nesting sites have been taken over. The sheer numbers of people

Green turtles young and old
Young green turtles (*Chelonia mydas*, above) with their characteristic black carapace and white belly shell. Several nights after breaking out of their shells, the hatchlings race to the sea, but on the way they may be eaten by birds, crabs and other animals. It is estimated that only one in a thousand survives to adulthood (below).

on the beaches, and the bars, sun beds and parasols, all pose a hazard to eggs incubating in the sand. And in the sea around the nesting areas, where the turtles wait for nightfall before swimming ashore, pleasure boats injure or even kill turtles by crashing into them.

When hatchlings emerge from the nest, usually at night, they instinctively use the reflection of the moon and stars on the sea to guide them to the water. But beach lighting disorientates them and they may spend long periods wandering about the shore, when they are particularly vulnerable to predators.

The huge amounts of rubbish left on the beach, together with the urban, industrial and agricultural waste dumped into the sea and then washed up on the shore, threaten turtles too, both directly and by preventing the animals digging their nests and laying their eggs. In the sea itself, turtles die from swallowing plastic, crude oil and other toxic substances. They also often become trapped or entangled in the thousands of tonnes of rubbish that are dumped in the Mediterranean, or in fishing gear that is lost at sea.

Caught on the line

Despite the turtles' protected status in almost all Mediterranean countries, every year, between 20,000 and 25,000 turtles are caught on the hooks of longline fishermen, particularly those of the Spanish and Italian fleets. Most are returned to sea with the hooks still embedded in them: some manage to expel the hook, but many of those that cannot, or that have been badly injured, will die.

A great number of turtles are caught by trawlers in the Gulf of Gabès, in southern Tunisia, an area used as foraging grounds by turtles that nest in Greece. And the increased use of driftnets and the presence of powerful 'pirate' Asian longliners in the Mediterranean both add to the risks the turtles have to face.

There is evidence, particularly in the region from southern Spain and the Balearic islands to Algeria, that Atlantic turtles cross into the Mediterranean at certain times of year. (This would explain how such a reduced number of eggs can maintain such a high proportion of captures without driving the species to extinction.) So turtle captures in the Mediterranean pose a threat to the Atlantic populations as well.

If Mediterranean sea turtles are to be saved from extinction, protected areas need to be established and enforced as a matter of urgency; tourist development, too, must be planned rationally, to keep its impact to a minimum. Equally importantly, ways must be found to reduce the huge numbers of incidental captures. Every Mediterranean country must ban the capture of sea turtles and the sale of all turtle products. And it is vital that all countries observe the agreements they have signed in recent years, concerning pollution of the sea and protection of marine wildlife.

At home in the sea
Like all sea turtles, the loggerhead (*Caretta caretta*, below) is a powerful swimmer, able to dive for long periods. Usually only female turtles leave the water, at nesting time.

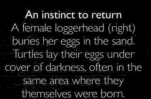

An instinct to return
A female loggerhead (right) buries her eggs in the sand. Turtles lay their eggs under cover of darkness, often in the same area where they themselves were born.

THE MEDITERRANEAN MONK SEAL

Thousands of centuries before the Mediterranean Sea became the cradle of human civilization, it was already inhabited by a creature that in the course of time has acquired the sad distinction of being considered one of the most endangered animals in the world: the Mediterranean monk seal (*Monachus monachus*).

This seal was originally present in 24 countries, including the whole of the Mediterranean Sea and the Black Sea, the Saharan coast and some Atlantic archipelagos. Today its only breeding sites are thought to be in Greece, the Western Sahara (some call this the Mauritanian group) and Madeira. Colonies are scattered from the Atlantic coast of Africa to the Black Sea, but it is impossible to say how many individuals each contains, and most colonies are declining. A very rough estimate puts the world population at no more than 300 or 400 individuals.

The Mediterranean monk seal is disappearing at a staggering rate. The obvious question is why. Not only does it lack predators other than humans; it has also shown over the centuries a surprising ability to adapt to changing conditions. When displaced by humans from the beaches where it used to bask and give birth, it found a new refuge in caves, often with an underwater entrance, and on rocky, cliffbound shores largely inaccessible from land.

Fishermen have played a part in the decline of the monk seal. Many fish stocks in the coastal areas of the Mediterranean have been severely depleted; the fishermen use the seals as scapegoats for the shortage of fish and persecute them.

Other factors too have contributed: the destruction of the seal's habitat, especially as a result of tourist development; the disturbance caused by large numbers of people visiting the seal caves; pollution; and the scarcity of food as a consequence of intensive fishing. And in the final months of 1990 in the western Mediterranean, a few monk seals were found dead with symptoms similar to those of the viral disease that killed thousands of harbour seals in the North Sea in the late 1980s. However, specialists could find no signs of the virus in the corpses, and the cause of the seals' death remains a mystery.

Creating a future

Many plans to save the Mediterranean seal have been discussed and approved in the last few decades. But very little action has followed the words. In some cases, funds allocated by international organizations to safeguard the monk seal have simply been wasted.

The need for real action to prevent the extinction of this species is now more urgent than ever before. It seems clear that campaigns to increase awareness of the dangers facing the seals would, at least, combat deliberate killing of seals, disturbance by people visiting the caves, and certain kinds of intensive fishing. These would be particularly effective when directed at the people who live in touch with the seals, especially fishermen but also children, policemen, lighthouse keepers, local authorities, conservation officials, and so on. But this will not be enough: the governments of the countries where monk seals survive must proceed

Profile of a seal
A Mediterranean monk seal (*Monachus monachus*, left) basks in the sun on a rocky shore. The monk seal is a coastal species and seeks out deep underwater caves where it can rest and reproduce. The female usually gives birth to only one pup, measuring 1 metre and weighing 15 or 20 kilograms: it can swim when four days old but will not be weaned until the age of four months. The coat is dark grey, in most cases with a large white patch on the belly (above right). An adult reaches metres in length and may weigh 300 kilograms (right). It dives for periods of about five minutes, to a depth of generally less than 30 metres, to pursue its prey – octopus, conger eel, grouper and other fish that live in the cracks of rocks.

urgently, with support from international organizations, to establish a network of well-protected reserves, in which all the disturbing activities are excluded.

There has been a series of proposals – from the south of France in particular – to breed monk seals in captivity; these have not so far been realized, nor even met with the unqualified support of seal experts. In any case, the priority for the monk seals must be to protect their habitat and improve their relationship with fishermen to ensure the safe future of existing populations, rather than to try to create new ones.

The last seal on Spanish soil
'Peluso' (above) lives on Spain's Chafarinas islands, off the African coast. In a celebrated operation in 1989, he was captured – and later set free – by conservationists and military veterinarians in order to remove a large rubber ring that had been tightening around his belly since he was a pup, causing a terrible wound.

THE WETLANDS

The Mediterranean coastal wetlands provide some of the region's richest habitats. Their abundant plant and animal life form rich feeding grounds that attract thousands of wintering and migrating waterfowl and waders and create invaluable nursery areas for fish.

The different kinds of wetland – salt marshes, estuaries and lagoons – are the geographical and biological meeting point of land and sea. The lagoons are particularly well developed in the Mediterranean: the virtual absence of tides favours life in these quiet, relatively shallow bodies of water, enclosed on one side by land and on the other by sand or shingle barriers, running parallel to the coast. Gaps in the barriers kept open by the tidal currents maintain the link with the sea.

Lagoons do not support many different species, but some of these are present in extraordinarily high numbers. Plant life flourishes here – it can be up to 15 times as productive as that in the sea. The reason for this is that nutrients build up in the calm, shallow water, stimulating growth. The plants themselves are food for microscopic plankton and copepods and, through the food web, for crustaceans, fish and birds.

Much of the vegetation is not eaten, but dies and sinks to the bottom. Here it and other organic remains, some brought in from outside the wetland, support a food web of worms and detritus-feeding fish, and a host of animals that feed on them in turn.

Life-giving water

From time to time, an influx of water, brought by tides or rivers, flushes away the debris-laden water, refreshing the lagoon environment and helping it to reach high levels of productivity.

However, occasionally, and in the warm regions especially, so much dead plant and animal material accumulates on the bottom that when it decomposes it outstrips the supply of oxygen and produces natural toxins, with the result that the entire community dies. But in the favoured conditions of the lagoon, even this catastrophe is only short term – before too long a fresh flow of water will bring the wetland back to life.

Over the centuries, many Mediterranean wetlands have disappeared, mainly through drainage to create land for agriculture. Even the few that remain are under threat, from development for housing and tourism. Some are seriously affected by agricultural fertilizers and pesticides, which run off from the land and settle in the sediments. Industrial pollution causes problems too. The semi-enclosed conditions of the lagoon mean that pollutants tend to accumulate in the sediments; from here they may enter the food web.

One of the biggest threats that faces the lagoon environment comes from erosion. As sand and gravel for the construction industry are dredged from the river beds, so fewer sediments are carried down to the coast, and the barrier between the sea and the lagoon eventually breaks down.

Even the sea itself is eating away at the wetlands, as the great prairies of the sea grass *Posidonia oceanica*, lying offshore, which have in the past broken the force of the waves, are gradually being destroyed.

Vanishing habitat
Wetlands are increasingly scarce in the Mediterranean, due to growing urbanization and the demand for agricultural land. This one (right), on Spain's Costa Blanca, is threatened by sewage from nearby hotels.

Winter wildlife
Wildfowl test the ice on a lagoon in winter (below right). In comparison to the sea, the wetlands are colder in winter, but warmer in summer.

Between land and sea
Coastal lagoons like this one (left) in France, to the west of the Camargue, offer ideal conditions for an extraordinary range of wildlife. The Camargue itself is visited by thousands of wintering, breeding and migrating birds, and is one of the few regular breeding sites in Europe and North Africa for the greater flamingo (*Phoenicopterus ruber*, below).

COUNTRY FILES

YUGOSLAVIA

Socijalisticka Federativna Republika Jugoslavije
Socialist Federal Republic of Yugoslavia

AREA 255,804 sq km. **LENGTH OF COASTLINE** 6,100 km (includes 4,020 km islands). **POPULATION** 23,864,000.

Yugoslavia is a federation of six republics: Serbia, Croatia, Slovenia, Bosnia-Hercegovina, Macedonia and Montenegro. Since multi-party politics was legalized, nationalist sentiments have threatened the cohesion of the formerly Communist federation.

THE PEOPLE

Yugoslavia's political organization reflects its ethnic diversity. The population consists of 36% Serbs, 20% Croats, 9% Bosnian Muslims, 8% Slovenes, 6% Macedonians and 8% Albanians, and other minorities. Religions too are mixed: 50% are Orthodox Christians, 30% Roman Catholic and 10% Muslim. Tensions between these communities are persistent, and have erupted into violence. About half of the Yugoslav population lives in towns; the capital, Belgrade, contains 1.47 million people.

THE ECONOMY

LABOUR FORCE 29% in agriculture, forestry and fisheries, 24% in mining and manufacturing, 9% in trade, 17% in services.
MAJOR EXPORTS Machinery and transport equipment, leather goods, textiles.
MAJOR IMPORTS Machinery, chemicals, iron, steel.
MINERAL RESOURCES Coal, iron, oil, copper, lead, zinc, bauxite, mercury.
CHIEF CROPS Cereals, sugar beet, sunflower oil, soya beans, tobacco.
VEHICLES 283,000 commercial, 2.9 million cars.

THE ENVIRONMENT

THE PRESENT Pollution from heavy metals, pesticides, fertilizers and untreated sewage contaminates the whole Yugoslavian coast, with particular 'hot spots' in the Krka estuary, Sibenik and Split. The north west has also been polluted by pesticide wastes from Italy. Only one town is 'considering' sewage treatment; the rest have none. Yugoslavia has one, reputedly unreliable, nuclear reactor, but plans to build four more reactors have been shelved following public concern. Yugoslavia has ten protected areas.
THE FUTURE The advent of greater political freedom in Yugoslavia may well bring environmental pressure groups and related political parties into existence, and possible closer ties with the EC will bring a measure of outside pressure to bear. However, the apparent fragility of the Yugoslav federation and a record of relative indifference to environmental issues suggest that ensuring political stability will take first call on the government's energies in the immediate future.

GREECE

Elliniki Dimokratia
Hellenic Republic

AREA 131,944 sq km. **LENGTH OF COAST** 15,000 km (includes 7,700 km islands). **POPULATION** 10,066,000.

Greece is a parliamentary democracy. The President is both head of state and ceremonial head of government. A Prime Minister forms a government from the majority party in the legislature.

THE PEOPLE

The Greeks have been an homogeneous people for over 3,000 years. Greece was part of the Muslim Turkish Ottoman empire from 1460 until 1827. A dispute over the sovereignty of Asia Minor was resolved only in 1922 with the establishment of Turkey in Europe. But tensions persist between the two countries, notably over the issues of Cyprus and oil under the Aegean.

THE ECONOMY

LABOUR FORCE 28% in agriculture; 29% in industry, 42% in services.
MAJOR EXPORTS Manufactured goods, fruit and vegetables, wine, tobacco, petroleum products. Tourism is vital to the Greek economy: nearly 8 million visitors annually contribute over 20% of the GDP.
MAJOR IMPORTS Machinery, vehicles, petroleum, consumer goods, chemicals, food.
MINERAL RESOURCES Bauxite, iron, oil, lignite, manganese.
CHIEF CROPS Cereals, rice, cotton, tobacco, olives, fruit.
VEHICLES 680,000 commercial, 1.4 million cars.

THE ENVIRONMENT

THE PRESENT Pollution from agriculture is serious, notably from fertilizer run-off, fertilizer factories and olive oil processing plants in the Ionian and Aegean seas; pig sewage threatens the Amvrakikos gulf. Both Greek and Yugoslavian wastes pollute the Thessaloniki gulf via the Vardar river. Air pollution is a major health problem in Athens. Oil pollution from tankers is serious in Greek waters. Zakynthos island is ostensibly protected as a haven for sea turtles but is being heavily developed. Monk seals are also at risk as protection programmes are not enforced. Coral fishing is now illegal except in two places but continues. Traditional inshore fishing is depleting breeding stocks. There are eight established protected areas.
THE FUTURE Greece has many environmental organizations; co-operation between them is increasing. A Green Party was formed before the EC elections in 1989, and Greenpeace opened a new office in Athens at the beginning of 1991; their first campaign concentrates on oil pollution. There is real official concern over Athens' polluted air, although measures to curtail motor traffic have met popular resistance.

ALBANIA
Republika Popullore Socialiste e Shqipërisë
People's Socialist Republic of Albania

AREA 28,748 sq km. **LENGTH OF COASTLINE** 400 km. **POPULATION** 3,270,000.

Until December 1990, Albania was a hard-line, one-party Communist state. In that month, other parties were legalized, but reformist demands continued.

THE PEOPLE
Albanians come from two basic ethnic groups, the Gegs of the north and Tosks of the south. The Tosk dialect is the official language. The population includes some 80,000 Greeks. Most ethnic Albanians are Muslim. All forms of religion were outlawed in 1967, but legitimized again in 1990. About a third of the population lives in towns – the major cities are the capital, Tirana (pop. 275,000), Durres (130,000) and Vlore (90,000). About 90% live on the coastal plain or nearby mountain plateaux.

THE ECONOMY
LABOUR FORCE 50% in agriculture; 50% in industry and commerce.
MAJOR EXPORTS Fuels, minerals and metals, food.
MAJOR IMPORTS Machinery, minerals, metals, fuel, construction materials, food.
MINERAL RESOURCES Chromium, coal, oil.
CHIEF CROPS Cereals, cotton, sugar beet, tobacco, potatoes, fruit.
VEHICLES No information available.

THE ENVIRONMENT
THE PRESENT Albania declined to join the Mediterranean Action Plan in the 1970s, but finally became a signatory in 1990. Atmospheric pollution from metallurgical, chemical and petroleum complexes is especially bad, while rivers and lakes are affected by untreated industrial and domestic waste. No measures exist to protect the environment, although the Kune wetlands at the mouth of the Drin are a nature reserve, as is the coastal lagoon at Divjaka. In central and southern Albania forest clearance to create farmland has caused soil erosion and has disastrously affected wildlife. Northern Albania remains relatively untouched because of the difficulty of the terrain, but the well-preserved wildlife (including bears) has become a haven for foreign hunters.

THE FUTURE Further progress towards political plurality is bound to reduce Albania's self-imposed international isolation, which will in turn bring pressure for more responsible environmental policies. Greater freedom of political expression may also see the emergence of 'green' politicians within Albania. But the outlook for the environment remains bleak.

Working the land
A group of workers creates new terracing for cultivation in Albania (below). Agriculture is an important part of the Albanian economy and, in the south of the country especially, land is always in demand for farming. Clearing the forests on such a scale means a disastrous loss of habitat for wildlife, and leads to serious soil erosion.

THE MEDITERRANEAN BALKANS

The Balkan nations bordering the Mediterranean have long been a paradox, for continuous political violence and the chequered history of democracy's birthplace in the south have unfolded against some of the world's most entrancing scenery.

Modern Greece includes several groups of Aegean and Ionian islands, of which the largest is Crete. The islands are typically mountainous, with narrow fertile coastal strips; of a total of over 2,000 only 169 are inhabited. The mainland too is almost uniformly mountainous, apart from the lowlands in Thrace, the central plain of Thessaly (watered by the Pinios river), the Arakhthos and Akheloos valleys and the north-western Peloponnese.

Mountains cover about threequarters of Albania, and in the north the land is heavily forested. (the Albanian name for the country means 'land of the eagles'). The Drin and Vijose rivers, with others, water the coastal plain. Nearly half the land is farmed. The climate is typical for the region – although in the mountains the temperature has sometimes dropped as low as -25°C.

About half of Yugoslavia is mountainous, with the Dinaric Alps rising almost straight out of the Adriatic along much of the coast, to become a wild limestone plateau in the east. Apart from industrial ports and some tourist resorts, the coast remains undeveloped. The largest cities are sited on the fertile inland plain watered by the Danube and its tributaries.

Green mountains
Parts of Yugoslavia – such as the Bay of Kodor (above) – show how the Mediterranean once looked when the hills were still forested. Nearby Lovcen National Park remains rich in wildlife, including imperial eagles and wild cats.

High plains
Mediterranean agriculture is largely limited to the coast or to hillside terraces, but in some countries high plateaux amid the mountains afford shelter for cultivation. One such plain (left) is near Feneos in the Peloponnese, southern Greece.

The secret country
Albania (above) was until recently one of the world's most impenetrable nations. Heavily forested and with more than half its people working on the land, much of the north is still unspoiled, although the south is marred by industry.

The bathing boar
A wild boar in Yugoslavia (top). These animals regularly seek out muddy waters, in which they rid themselves of parasites. Heavily hunted all over Europe, boars have nevertheless survived in large numbers where there is still forest to give them cover.

SOUTH AND EAST
THE KEY TO THE FUTURE

THE FUTURE of the Mediterranean will not be decided only by what happens in the rich, powerful and highly industrialized countries of western Europe. It will, rather, be decided in the nations of the south and east of the region – for it is here that the population is growing fastest, where water is most scarce, where demand for food has already far outstripped what local agriculture can supply, and where there is greatest potential for industrial development. How the southern and eastern countries tackle these problems, and how the affluent nations of Europe respond in turn, will affect the whole Mediterranean region, and determine whether its future is to be bearable for both people and the environment.

The heart of the matter

The three most pressing problems facing the south and east of the region are the rapidly growing population, the scarcity of water, and the degradation of agricultural land. The most visible of these is the burgeoning number of people, which is growing at over 3 percent per annum in some countries, leading to a doubling of 1990 population levels within 25 years. In order to solve the immediate economic problems that such numbers pose, countries will understandably seek to industrialize as quickly and cheaply as possible.

The pressure of so many people will also put huge strains on supplies of already scarce water, for direct consumption and for agriculture and services. Industrialization will only intensify that demand, as will programmes to 'industrialize' farming, increased use of fertilizers and pesticides, and plans to extend irrigation schemes and agricultural land as a whole. All these factors will tend to increase the rate of soil erosion and desertification. If, as seems likely, the future of the region resembles its recent past, the apparent solution to the difficulties faced by the south and east will be only short-lived, and will leave more and worse problems to be solved. And in the process it will have added to the already crushing burden on the environment.

New polluters for old

The biggest polluters of the Mediterranean today are the sea's most heavily industrialized nations: Italy, France and Spain. These three will undoubtedly head the league for years to come. But even if pollution from the north-western Mediterranean gradually reduces, industrial developments in the south and east are likely to increase the burden on the sea. For while the west is slowly adopting machinery, plant and production methods designed to be less damaging to the environment, western industry is at the same time cutting the costs of those improvements by selling its old, polluting plant to less-developed countries. And the buyers feel they have little choice but to accept it, because the new, 'clean' technology on offer is priced too high.

The results of this policy can already be seen in the pollution 'hot spots' of North Africa. In Tunisia, for example, the phosphate industry established by the French in Sfax has expanded since independence in 1956 to nearby Gabès, where a unique coastal oasis is now severely threatened. Fish in the bay of Sfax are riddled with spots and scabs. People who live in the area reputedly suffer a higher incidence of pulmonary disease than anywhere else in Tunisia

The receiving end
The Nile (below, in the Delta at Damanhur) serves as a source of water for virtually all domestic needs, from washing clothes to drinking, for many of those who live nearby. But the Nile is polluted with sewage, and the fertile land along the length of the river and in the delta itself is heavily treated with pesticides and fertilizers, much of which wash into the river. The few water courses in other countries in the south and east suffer yet worse effects, for they are tiny compared to the Nile.

Tomorrow belongs to them
The rising generation in the southern and eastern countries of the Mediterranean (left and right) faces a future that holds formidable economic problems. Although the birth rate in the area is falling drastically from a 1980s average of about five children per woman, the overall increase in the population will mean that in some North African countries nearly half the population will be under 14 years of age in 2025, while the total for the south and east may exceed 350 million. Such conditions will accompany an inevitable demand for higher standards of living throughout the region. If the future is to be assured for the people of the area, economic development must take full account of both scarce and natural resources and the effects it is likely to have on the environment.

– and they fear that local industry may be responsible. Although there is a government programme designed to stop all discharges of industrial waste in Sfax, treatment facilities have yet to be completed.

Similar problems have developed in the eastern Mediterranean since the 1960s, as the coasts have suffered from industrial and tourist developments. As in North Africa, there are still only 'hot spots' here – in Thessaloniki in Greece, and Izmir and Iskenderun in Turkey, for example. But if these indicate what 'development' will bring to the whole of the southern and eastern Mediterranean, the outlook is truly grave.

The crisis on the land

Farmers have been busy in the fields of the eastern Mediterranean for perhaps 10,000 years, and pests have always caused problems. But the chemical panacea offered by western industry in the past 40 years has proved to be no cure at all, as the pesticides kill beneficial species as well, and the destructive pests gradually become immune to their poison. Millions of tonnes of pesticides are exported from the west to the 'developing' countries of the Mediterranean. What makes this worse is that many of them are considered too dangerous to be used in the countries that supply them.

One of the greatest crises faced by farmers in the southern and eastern Mediterranean is the loss of productive land. The increasing demand for housing and tourist accommodation has led to a complete disregard for the impact of construction on vital agricultural areas. The problem is often compounded by grandiose industrial schemes that have not been properly thought out. In one gigantic project, intended to supply the European paper industry with wood, international institutions funded the planting of millions of eucalyptus trees in Algeria. The trees did not, however, adapt to their new

Fuelling pollution
A petrochemical complex at Skikda in Algeria (above) adds to the contamination of the Mediterranean. As the countries of the south and east continue to industrialize, energy production will increase, as will the pollution that accompanies the burning of fossil fuels. This need not be inevitable, if nations explore ways to use energy more efficiently and develop the use of alternative fuels.

environment. They took water from indigenous plants, brought a new kind of woodworm into the region, and then failed as a crop – so contributing to the desertification of an area already poor in fertile land.

From bad to worse

People who live and work in the area believe pollution is already taking its toll. Dead fish have been reported on the surface in places as far apart as Cyprus and Algeria. Greek and Cypriot fishermen report sponges suffering from disease and falling to pieces. A similar phenomenon has struck Tunisian corals. Some kinds of sea urchin have totally disappeared from Malta.

The special difficulties confronting the south and east will not only help to worsen effects like these throughout the region; they will intensify and enlarge the problems those areas already face. Demands for energy will rise, increasing pollution from oil as well as from other sources. Nuclear power, although being developed by some nations in the area, is not a clean or safe alternative. More people will add more sewage to a sea that cannot absorb it.

Particularly alarming is the trade in toxic waste in the region. It is difficult to establish its true extent, but the industrialized world does undoubtedly export hazardous waste to the less-developed world. In one case, barrels of waste were simply abandoned on the Lebanese coast. Toxic cargoes also move regularly through the Suez Canal. The African states and Turkey have tried to get a ban on the export of such waste, but this has been blocked by France.

Which way forward?

As populations in the south and east continue to multiply and their economic demands rise, they will be more and more exposed to the negative aspects of industrialization. Poor countries have already shown their vulnerability to cash incentives, even when that means becoming a dump for toxic waste. They will increasingly be at the mercy of western industry selling them cheap, polluting equipment – just as western industry will be unable to resist the opportunity to expand into cheap locations with low-paid labour.

The alternative is to make both information and technology readily available to the south and east, in order to ensure that industrial development there observes environmental standards that are at least as rigorous as those now being introduced in the north west. This would be more beneficial to all concerned than any conventional aid programme.

Whichever course is taken, all countries – north, south, east, west – must know that they can reap tomorrow only the fruits of what they sow today.

PART

When conservationists, scientists and journalists alike began to talk of the 'death' of the Mediterranean at the end of the 1960s, there seemed little doubt that, if no solutions were found to the growing assault on the Mediterranean environment, then the fate of this sea would be sealed forever.

The United Nations responded in 1975 by establishing the Mediterranean Action Plan – a series of legally binding agreements to bring various kinds of pollution under control and to improve wildlife protection. Remarkably, by 1990, it had involved all Mediterranean states to some extent – bringing to the same table countries as diverse as Israel and Syria, Greece and Turkey, to discuss the protection of the sea that they all share. The Mediterranean Action Plan has also in part inspired other measures, to control offshore oil pollution and, to a far more limited extent, fishing. It has also encouraged bodies such as the World Bank, the European Investment Bank and the European Community to give loans or grants for environmental projects.

But 15 years after the start of the action plan, its limitations are glaringly apparent. Although many agreements have been made, their implementation has been shockingly poor. Governments still lack a sense of urgency about the ever-worsening state of the sea.

But change will come: when they realize that it is cheaper to prevent environmental damage than to try to deal with its aftermath.

A fountain of troubles
A dredger pumps sandy sediment from the seabed onto a Spanish beach to reduce erosion. But this can deprive other areas of sediments, and actually increase erosion. Dredging also changes the physical nature of the seabed, which can affect fish and other marine life. In some cases, the sediments are polluted, and disturbing them re-releases the pollutants. Environmental problems are rarely simple and cannot be tackled successfully by piecemeal measures.

POLITICS
PLANS WITHOUT ACTION

WHEN UNEP ADOPTED the Mediterranean for its first ever Regional Seas Programme in the mid 1970s it knew that the degradation of the sea could be halted only by fully integrating environmental concerns into national plans for economic development. But this was such an ambitious aim to present right at the start of the programme, that UNEP concentrated first on getting a framework for international agreement and funding for research, targeting two areas – dumping at sea and oil pollution, which all countries saw as priorities – for specific action.

Representatives from all coastal states except Syria and Albania met at Barcelona in February 1975 to approve the details of the Mediterranean Action Plan (MAP). The formal agreement, the Convention for the Protection of the Mediterranean Sea against Pollution, was signed by 12 states in February 1976 (all Mediterranean states and the European Community have now signed the convention – including Albania, which signed in 1990). Two protocols (themselves legally binding) were also adopted. The first committed the countries to ban the dumping at sea of certain dangerous substances – the 'black' list; and to regulate by permit the dumping of substances believed to be less dangerous – the 'grey' list. The second protocol concerned emergency action in the event of spills of oil and other harmful substances from ships.

Neither of the protocols has lived up to its promise. Some countries have not even established an authority to issue dumping permits, and few notify the Convention secretariat of licences granted or of the quantity and nature of material to be dumped – which makes it impossible to assess how far the undertakings are fulfilled. Similarly, only eight Mediterranean countries have produced plans to cope with accidental spills, and of these only a few have the necessary equipment to put them into practice.

Pollution from the land

In 1976 UNEP began to draw up a more controversial protocol dealing with pollution from land-based sources. It commissioned a systematic survey to assess the quantity of pollutants entering the Mediterranean from land. But the information barely existed, and researchers were forced to estimate levels of pollution indirectly from production and employment statistics that were themselves deficient. Nonetheless, the results were enough to show that pollution from land-based sources was a huge problem. The report concluded that 85 percent of all Mediterranean pollution originated on land and that 80-85 percent of this came from the rivers. It also found that less than 20 percent of sewage directly entering the Mediterranean received any treatment beforehand. When the report was released in September 1977, it described pollution loads for each of ten regions rather than for individual states, because some countries were concerned that they would be singled out as particularly bad polluters, and would suffer accordingly.

The 'Med X' report should have shocked governments into action, yet negotiations for the land-based sources protocol dragged on for three years. Despite the report's findings, France and Italy initially sought to omit river-based pollution (the Rhône and the Po are major channels of pollution to the Mediterranean). These two countries also objected to the inclusion of

En route to the Med
Huge amounts of industrial effluent are still discharged into Mediterranean rivers such as the Rhône (left). The prevention of pollution from land-based sources – both industrial and domestic – was delayed for many years, because it was assumed that it was relatively unimportant.

The first alarm
In the 1960s the enormous growth in oil cargoes shipped along the Suez Canal (below) and through the Mediterranean led to a huge increase in oil pollution. This threatened the growing tourist industry in the region – and the revenue from it. Individual states could do little to combat the problem because the source of the pollution lay outside national boundaries. In the mid 1970s, encouraged by the United Nations Environment Programme, the Mediterranean countries began their first co-operative attempts at dealing with the problem.

pollution carried through the atmosphere. Eventually they gave way on both issues (although at the end of 1990 the details of how to regulate airborne pollution of the Mediterranean had yet to be worked out).

Control of land-based sources of pollution was to be based on the EC's black and grey lists and on similar regulations drawn up by the Paris Commission for the northeast Atlantic. But the measures to be used became a subject of intense debate: northwestern Mediterranean states wanted the same, fixed standards of discharge for all, while those of the less-industrialized south and east argued for ambient standards, set according to the level of existing pollution, which would allow them to bring their pollution levels up to those of the north before taking action. A compromise was eventually reached: fixed emission standards would apply for substances on the black list, and ambient standards for the grey list.

The protocol, agreed in 1980, is not intended to come into full effect until 1995, by which time 50 different measures for pollution control have to be set. However, by 1990 only eight had been agreed: for mercury in water and in fish; for faecal bacteria in bathing and shellfish waters; for used lubricating oils (which contain heavy metals and synthetic chemicals), cadmium, orga-notin chemicals (used in paint to stop marine life growing on ships), and halogenated hydrocarbons (HHCs). And countries have again been reluctant to put their paper agreements into practice, and have failed to supply the MAP secretariat with such information as sources of pollution, discharge permits issued, or amounts discharged. Five countries have not yet signed the protocol: Lebanon, Malta, Libya, Syria and Yugoslavia.

Areas in need of protection

The most recent protocol of the Barcelona Convention is that for Specially Protected Areas, which was set up in 1982 and entered into force in 1986. It requires signatories to provide information on existing marine reserves and to identify areas and species in need of protection. Action plans have been agreed to safeguard monk seals and sea turtles. Mediterranean countries have

Stuck for a solution
Slow-moving traffic (above left), enclosed streets, strong sunlight and high temperatures combine to make exhaust fumes a health hazard in many Mediterranean urban areas. Countries have failed so far to reach international agreement on how to tackle atmospheric pollution.

Belated review
The environment often takes second place in development programmes. The water supply to Akrotiri Lake, Cyprus's most important wetland, was cut off by a dam (above), built with the aid of the World Bank. Yet an assessment of the impact on the environment was commissioned only after the dam had been built.

also agreed to take all necessary measures to protect the *Posidonia* seagrass meadows, in particular to prevent the damage caused by trawling, and recently plans were made to give proper protection to dolphins and whales.

With this protocol, MAP widened its scope from the original focus on pollution – which was essential if the Mediterranean ecosystems were to be saved. But attempts to create new specially protected areas meet stiff opposition, generally because the plans ignore local communities, failing to create jobs in the management of the site or explain why it deserves protection, but also because the proposed sites are usually in demand for development by the powerful tourist industry. Five countries have still to sign the SPA protocol – Lebanon, Libya, Monaco, Morocco and Syria.

The Blue Plan

UNEP's attempt to achieve its most ambitious goal of getting countries to adopt integrated planning took form as the Blue Plan. This project tried to envisage the environmental consequences of various trends in development by the years 2000 and 2025. The areas of study included: water resources, industry, energy consumption, health, population growth and migration, land use, tourism, cross-cultural relations and environmental values.

The Blue Plan's conclusions were frightening: unless current development trends were immediately altered in order to reverse the degradation and depletion of natural resources, the Mediterranean would suffer environmental catastrophe, with unavoidable consequences for the already fragile political and social situation in the region.

But most countries ignored the report's implications and, as yet, no state can claim to have truly integrated an environmental dimension into its long-

Live and let live
Some 6,000 sea turtles are deliberately caught each year for food. They are kept alive, trussed up and tied to a pole (above) to immobilize them for the duration of the trip to shore. While such attitudes to wildlife persist, turtles and other species risk following the fate of the monk seal. When the photograph below was taken, in Majorca in 1922, monk seals were abundant and believed to be immune to the effects of human actions. Now the seal population is reduced to a relic, and the animals are vulnerable to both natural and human disasters.

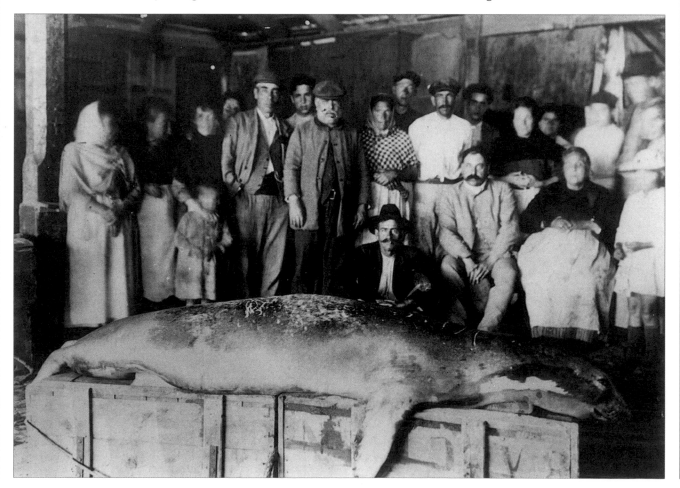

term economic planning. Although some countries intend to use Blue Plan material for the major UN Conference on Environment and Development in 1992, experience suggests that this is unlikely to lead to action.

The Genoa Declaration

In 1985 MAP countries met in Genoa to assess progress in the first decade. The states acknowledged the need to increase their efforts on behalf of the Mediterranean and, in the Genoa Declaration, set out ten goals to be achieved by 1995. One target was to build sewage plants in all coastal cities with over 100,000 inhabitants, and to provide 'appropriate' treatment plants for those with a population greater than 10,000. Another was to create 50 new protected areas, under the aegis of the specially protected areas protocol.

However, the greatest failure was that still nothing was done to compel countries to implement these and past agreements, and by 1987 the programme was already falling behind in its schedule.

BEYOND THE ACTION PLAN

The Mediterranean Action Plan lies at the centre of international efforts to protect the Mediterranean. Other bodies are also involved, but the failure to follow words with action is just the same. Not all countries have ratified the annexes of the International Convention for the Prevention of Pollution from Ships (MARPOL); and only 9 of 19 oil-loading terminals have facilities to handle waste oil. And although important wetland sites such as Lake Ichkeul, in Tunisia, are in theory protected by the Ramsar Convention, they are still being destroyed by schemes to create land for agriculture and development.

On fishing, despite specific initiatives such as those by Spain, Italy and Tunisia to ban driftnet fishing, there is still no systematic framework for international regulation. The General Fisheries Council for the Mediterranean comes closest to providing this, but is limited to making recommendations on such matters as mesh size, fishing methods, and closed seasons. For the most part, regulations are drawn up nationally and enforcement is weak. Moreover, these cover only inshore waters; a free-for-all, for Mediterranean and non-Mediterranean fleets alike, continues in international waters.

One stumbling block for all environmental projects in the region has been lack of funds. In January 1988, the World Bank and European Investment Bank launched a joint programme to provide finance for environmental protection in the Mediterranean (called the EPM), with the declared aim of placing the minimum impact on the economies of developing countries.

The first major commitment of funds came in April 1990, when the two banks and the EC agreed to set aside $1.5 billion to support the Nicosia Charter – an initiative sponsored by the EC and endorsed by most MAP nations. The charter reiterated the aims of the 1985 Genoa Declaration and committed the countries to establish a framework for enforcement of earlier agreements, assisted by taxation and other financial incentives. But the mechanism for compelling countries to carry out their legal obligations is still not clear, and the timetable for action now stretches over 35 years. And although financial commitments were made – for instance, the EC agreed to pay for 25 sewage plants in coastal cities – funding may yet turn out to be a problem. The World Bank has a reputation for insisting on conditions for loans that give it a large say in the running of a nation's economy. And the terms of some of the EC's grants require that part of the funds be found elsewhere. For some countries, supporting half of the investment may be just as impossible as bearing the total cost.

Pollution folly
A new but abandoned dredger (below) in the Turkish bay of Izmir stands as a monument to a misguided attempt to find a short-term solution to an environmental problem. Izmir Bay is heavily polluted by local industry. With a guarantee of aid from the World Bank, the authorities acquired the dredger to collect contaminated sediments and dump them out at sea – an intention hardly in the spirit of the Barcelona Convention and its associated protocol. In any case, the Turkish authorities and the bank fell out over funding and the project ground to a halt. Meanwhile, the companies that are the source of the problem discharge their pollutants unabated.

Fishing for solutions
The fishing industry in the Mediterranean is beset by problems. Information is poor and the range of research is limited. Attempts to 'manage' fishing rarely take social and economic conditions into account, or recognize the complications caused by constant changes in policy. The result is rules that rarely command respect and that are seldom enforced.

THE FUTURE

UNEP can claim some success with the Mediterranean Action Plan. But ultimately only national governments have the power to save the Mediterranean, and it is time for them to accept their responsibility. They must find a mechanism with which to enforce legally binding agreements; without it those agreements are degenerating into a charade. Similarly, they must ensure that funds are available for environmental programmes. The annual international budget for the Mediterranean Action Plan is only $5 million (the value of just one sixth of an average tanker load of oil), divided among all countries, many of which have fallen behind in making even these payments.

Then there are new specific measures that need to be taken. A new legal instrument, established within the Barcelona Convention, to prevent the serious problems caused by the export of hazardous waste is urgently needed. The known dangers of the substances on the black list, including HHCs and organophosphorus pesticides, are so great that the MAP countries should phase out their use rather than try to regulate their disposal. And, one way or another, long-term planning for environmental management, including protection of wildlife and habitats, and integrating tourism, development and fishing, must become a reality.

All countries and all ports must implement the terms of MARPOL to ensure that safe reception facilities are available for all waste oil, and that adequate enforcement mechanisms are set in place to prevent deliberate discharge at sea. Hopes for improved regulation of fishing are largely centred on the extension to the Mediterranean of the EC's Common Fisheries Policy. This will undoubtedly prove difficult, but some international regulation must be better than the near anarchy that currently exists in the Mediterranean.

The need for a new approach

Beyond these specific measures there is a pressing need for a general realignment of policy in the Mediterranean to reflect the discovery that the environment is far less resilient than we thought, even ten years ago. Indeed, UNEP has now adopted the 'precautionary principle', whose essence is that if

Time for a change
A burning rubbish dump on the beach at the Spanish enclave of Melilla in North Africa (below left) is a graphic reminder of the wasteful habits we have acquired. Unless there is a radical change in policy to reduce to a minimum the amount of waste produced, the volume of rubbish here will be dwarfed by the mountain that will exist by the time these children are adults.

Thought before action
A power station alongside tourist facilities near Iraklion, Crete (below right), illustrates the lack of thought that goes into much coastal development. It is extremely unlikely that the effect of either project on the local environment was considered before work went ahead. In future, much more emphasis will have to be placed on integrated coastal planning, which seeks to avoid both conflicts of interest and environmental damage.

there is any suspicion that a human action might damage the environment then that action should be stopped – until it can be proved to be safe.

Although the Barcelona Convention now incorporates the precautionary principle, there is little sign of it being put into practical effect. Even in agreements as recent as the Nicosia Charter, no mention is made of the precautionary principle, and there is still the old emphasis on, for example, finding the best means of disposing of waste rather than exploring ways to promote the application of clean production, as also recommended by UNEP.

Behind all this lie the fundamental reasons for environmental degradation – the exploitation of people and the natural world – and these need to be honestly appraised. In September 1990 the Spanish and Italian governments proposed a conference whose aim would be to enhance co-operation and development within the region, and address issues that have so far been given little attention, including human rights and disarmament, as well as more 'traditional' environmental issues. This Conference on Security and Co-operation in the Mediterranean would include all Mediterranean countries, as well as those of the Black Sea, the Middle East, Mauritania and the USA.

Whatever comes of this proposal – and it is by no means sure that it will live up to expectations – the Mediterranean countries must now seriously reassess their attitude. A dangerous complacency has crept in and people are too ready to talk about the sea having been saved, while ignoring the almost universal failure, time and time again, to carry through the most basic of changes. Real change will come only when those in power have become convinced that environmental protection is necessary and urgent. Without it, the Mediterranean will continue its slide into chaos.

Making the connection
Scenes such as this Greek store selling natural sponges are part of the attraction of the Mediterranean. Buying an individual sponge may seem innocuous enough, but such is the demand that sponge populations in many areas have been severely depleted – to the cost in one way or another of wildlife, local people and tourists. The lack of awareness of the link between individual actions and environmental damage is at the heart of most of the Mediterranean's problems.

COUNTRY FILES

ITALY

Repubblica Italiana
Italian Republic

AREA 301,250 sq km (includes Sicily, Sardinia and Elba, as well as the smaller islands). **LENGTH OF COASTLINE** 8,000 km. **POPULATION** 57,657,000.

Italy is a parliamentary democracy. The President is head of state; a Chairman of the Council of Ministers is head of government. There are two houses of parliament, elected by proportional representation.

THE PEOPLE

Italy's population includes small minorities of Germans, Slovenes and Albanians. Nearly 75% of the population live in towns. The major cities are the capital, Rome (pop. 2.8 million), Milan (1.8 million), Naples (1.2 million), Turin (1.05 million), Genoa (740,000) and Palermo (716,000). There are considerable economic and cultural differences among the regions and islands.

THE ECONOMY

LABOUR FORCE 5% in agriculture; 32% in industry and commerce; 58% in government and services.
MAJOR EXPORTS Machinery and transport equipment, chemicals, textiles, metals (Italy produces 25% of the world's mercury), food. Tourists – approaching 20 million annually – are economically very important.
MAJOR IMPORTS Engineering, chemicals, food, metals.
MINERAL RESOURCES Natural gas, oil, marble, mercury, coal, lignite, sulphur, iron, lead, zinc, aluminium.
CHIEF CROPS Grapes, olives, citrus fruit, vegetables, wheat, rice.
VEHICLES 1.9 million commercial, 23.3 million cars.

THE ENVIRONMENT

THE PRESENT Attempts to export toxic waste to Third World countries have generated more than one scandal. Much waste is dumped into rivers and lakes. Fertilizer run-off, urban and industrial wastes pour down the Po river into the Adriatic, which has suffered severe algal blooms as a result. Coasts have become so contaminated by raw sewage that Italian authorities have raised the official 'safe' level of bacteria in seawater. Italian waters are overfished. Heavy tourism has added to environmental problems. There are ten coastal, wetland or marine protected areas.
THE FUTURE Environmental issues are gaining ground in Italy. As a result of a referendum held in the wake of the Chernobyl disaster, nuclear power stations were closed. Trade unions are increasingly concerned over pollution; the Green Party has seats in parliament. However, business interests are very powerful, and have been known to develop designated 'green' areas for tourism or business. Italy continues to permit nuclear weapons on its territory: Naples and La Maddalena in Sardinia are major US navy bases.

FRANCE

La République Française
French Republic

AREA 547,026 sq km (includes Corsica). **MEDITERRANEAN COAST** 1,700 km. **POPULATION** 56,400,000.

France is a democracy. The President is an elected head of state and of the executive, and appoints a Council of Ministers, headed by a Prime Minister, to form a government. The parliament has two houses.

THE PEOPLE

The French population includes a number of regional ethnic groups: besides French speakers, minorities speak Breton, Basque, Alsatian German, Flemish, Italian, Catalan and (among immigrant Algerians and Moroccans) Arabic and Berber. Nearly 80% of the population live in towns; the major cities include the capital, Paris (pop. 8,707,000 including suburbs), Lyons (1.2 million), Marseilles (1.1 million), and Lille (940,000).

THE ECONOMY

LABOUR FORCE 9% in agriculture, 45% in industry and commerce, 46% in services.
MAJOR EXPORTS Farm products, machinery, chemicals, vehicles, textiles and clothing.
MAJOR IMPORTS Machinery, crude oil, minerals, chemicals, agricultural products, vehicles.
MINERAL RESOURCES Oil, coal, iron, bauxite.
CHIEF CROPS Cereals, rice, fruit, sugar beet.
VEHICLES 3.9 million commercial, 21.9 million cars.

THE ENVIRONMENT

THE PRESENT High concentrations of heavy metals from the Rhône pollute the Gulf of Lyons. Sewage is rarely treated before being discharged into the sea. Pesticides are extensively used. Nuclear power stations across the country produce about 65% of France's electricity. France has its own nuclear weapons, and hosts nuclear-armed and -powered ships from NATO navies. Laws governing pollution exist but are often vague. The Camargue National Reserve is the most famous of ten marine and coastal protected areas.
THE FUTURE France's 5,000-strong Mediterranean fishing fleet is supported by subsidies for technical innovations and improvements; these are having mixed environmental effects. Despite the country's tendency to defend its perceived national interests, environmental issues are now gaining ground. However, it is likely that French nuclear policy will remain unchanged, and that agricultural over-production, which owes much to fertilizers and pesticides, will remain fiercely protected.

SPAIN

Reino de España
Kingdom of Spain

AREA 504,782 sq km (including Balearic Islands, Canary Islands and North African enclaves). MEDITERRANEAN COAST 2,600 km. POPULATION 39,623,000.

Spain is a constitutional monarchy. The President of the Government is chosen by the leading party in the bicameral legislature. Spain's 17 autonomous regions have their own governments and parliaments.

THE PEOPLE

The people of Spain comprise four basic cultural and language groups: Castilian-speaking (73%), Catalans (16%), Galicians (8%) and Basques (2.5%). About 75% of the Spanish people live in towns: major cities include the capital, Madrid (pop. 3.5 million), Barcelona (2 million), Valencia (775,000) and Seville (645,000).

THE ECONOMY

LABOUR FORCE 16% in agriculture, 24% in industry and commerce, 52% in services.
MAJOR EXPORTS Fruit and farm produce, iron and steel products, footwear, textiles, vehicles, refined petroleum. Tourism is economically vital – Spain has 50.5 million visitors annually.

MAJOR IMPORTS Cotton, tobacco, cellulose, food, fertilizers, machinery, vehicles, wool, oil products.
MINERAL RESOURCES Coal, iron, tungsten, copper, zinc, lead, iron, uranium, mercury.
CHIEF CROPS Cereals, grapes, citrus fruit, vegetables, olives.
VEHICLES 1.7 million commercial, 9.7 million cars.

THE ENVIRONMENT

THE PRESENT Much of the Mediterranean coast, and the Gulf of Cadiz, whose water feeds the Mediterranean, is polluted with heavy metals. Spanish fishing methods are affecting sea turtles, dolphins and *Posidonia* sea grass. Soil erosion is a particular problem; reforestation projects have used inappropriate species such as eucalyptus. Nine nuclear reactors are in operation, and NATO nuclear warships visit Spanish ports, although this is technically illegal. Pesticides and fertilizers are heavily used by farmers. Six marine, wetland and coastal areas are protected.

THE FUTURE Environmental issues are a matter of constant public concern. There are many environmental groups and these have won some major victories. The Spanish government regards nuclear power as 'transitory'. Sewage treatment is improving. Sea turtles enjoy national protection, although enforcement is often lax; regional legislation in Andalucia, in the south, protects all marine mammals.

MONACO

Monte Carlo (right) rises out of the sea, scarcely distinguishable from its neighbour Monaco-ville, capital of Monaco. The land, a high promontory between France and Italy, is entirely built over – there is no agriculture. The principality of Monaco is a constitutional monarchy, whose electorate is restricted to true-born Monégasques, who comprise about 16 percent of the 29,000-strong population. The chief Minister of State is a French civil servant. The country is under French protection and, should the sovereign die without an heir, Monaco would be incorporated into France. Monaco's income derives from tourism (about 1.5 million visitors annually), its state-owned casino, and chemicals and precision instruments industries. Monaco's impact on the environment is minuscule compared to that of the industrial giants that flank this tiny 188-hectare nation.

THE NORTHWEST

The countries of the northwestern Mediterranean are the most highly developed in the region. Yet their essential nature is still 'typically' Mediterranean.

Italy is divided by the Apennine mountains running north to south, with a broad coastal plain on either side. The plain of Lombardy in the north east, watered by Italy's largest river, the Po, is particularly fertile. The coastline is largely devoted to tourism.

Northern and western France form a wide plain. Five major rivers and the mountainous central plateau define the rest of the country: the Aude and the Rhône (one of the region's largest rivers) empty into the Mediterranean. France's southern coastline is almost entirely urbanized apart from the Camargue, at the mouth of the Rhône.

Most of Spain consists of a high, arid plateau, divided by mountains and river valleys. The coastal lowlands, except on the Atlantic, are very narrow. Yet, because of irrigation, Spain is remarkably fertile. The Ebro is the Mediterranean's third largest river. Spain's Balearic islands attract droves of tourists, although much wildlife survives on the undeveloped fringes.

Away from it all
Majorca (above), the largest of the Spanish Balearic Islands, is the Mediterranean's most popular holiday resort. But some parts of the island are remarkably undeveloped and still largely unspoiled.

Island of beauty
Tranquil waters at Cala Domestica on Sardinia's west coast (above). Sardinia is one of the largest Mediterranean islands, second in size only to Sicily. Much of its rolling countryside is uncultivated and covered with forest and *maquis*, the fragrant vegetation typical of the region, making it a haven for wildlife and flowering plants.

The summer falcon
The entire world population of Eleonora's falcon (*Falco eleonorae* left) – about 4,500 pairs – breeds exclusively in the Mediterranean region after wintering mainly in Madagascar. The falcons nest in about 100 colonies – Italy's largest is in Sardinia – on cliffs and rocky coasts, breeding late to feed their young on small birds that are migrating in autumn.

An island storm
In winter, Mediterranean weather can be both violent and unpredictable, as the combination of sea currents and island land masses helps to create numerous microclimates. Here, Ajaccio on the west coast of Corsica (left) is lashed by wind and rain.

Under a burning sun
The Chaine de l'Estaque (below), west of Marseilles, seen looking north west towards the Camargue, after a fire in August 1989 denuded the hills. To the east lie the rugged heights and fertile valleys of Provence.

PART
4

When the Greenpeace flagship *Sirius* slipped through the Strait of Gibraltar and into the Mediterranean on 9 May 1986, public concern about the state of the sea was relatively low. Its waters seemed as sparkling as they had ever done, for until recently much of what threatened the sea was invisible to the casual visitor. But the Mediterranean was in a perilous state — and time was running out for anyone who wanted to see the sea healthy again.

The arrival of the *Sirius* signalled the beginning of Greenpeace's campaign of political lobbying, educational publicity and direct actions — backed as ever by meticulous research — on behalf of the Mediterranean. During the first five years of the campaign, the urgency of Greenpeace's message became all too apparent as such disasters as algal blooms and dolphin deaths made headline news, and became grim allies in the environmentalists' cause.

By the end of 1990, Greenpeace had achieved some remarkable successes — not only in helping to bring the crisis in the Mediterranean to public notice, but also in altering government policy in more than one country. Most heartening of all, the organization has managed to spread word of the sea's plight further afield, opening a new office in Greece and making contact with people and governments in Malta, Cyprus and North Africa. At least partly because of Greenpeace's campaign, there is probably greater hope today that the Mediterranean nations, despite their enormous political differences, will remain united in their practical attempts to protect their unique environment.

Without fear or favour
Greenpeace volunteers show scant regard for their own safety as they climb the anchor chain of a Soviet nuclear-armed warship off the Greek island of Kythera in 1989. Actions like this have also been mounted against the US navy, and not only draw attention to the risks in taking nuclear reactors to sea, but make a vital diplomatic point: Greenpeace do not take political sides in their campaigns.

GREENPEACE
THE MEDITERRANEAN CAMPAIGN

WITHIN A WEEK of first arriving in the Mediterranean in May 1986, the Greenpeace flagship *Sirius* was in action, harassing the nuclear waste transporter *Mediterranean Shearwater* in the Strait of Gibraltar as it made its way loaded with spent radioactive fuel from Italy to the UK. Seven days later, the *Sirius*'s crew were dropping artificial 'reefs' into the sea around Malaga to foil illegal trawling. The next day the target was a ship stripping red coral with the infamous 'Italian bar'. On 6 June, Greenpeace activists were protesting against the destruction of the wildlife sanctuary of Cabrera, off Majorca, by Spanish military manoeuvres. The new Greenpeace Mediterranean campaign was wasting no time in getting its message across.

That message was simple enough: the Mediterranean governments were doing little or nothing to implement their own agreements under UNEP's Mediterranean Action Plan, which had been launched in 1975: ten years of good intentions had achieved little in stemming the flood of pollution and the destruction of wildlife in the sea. All Greenpeace's actions in the Mediterranean have been designed to drive this point home, to arouse public opinion and to embarrass governments into backing their public words with positive measures.

In 1984, Greenpeace set up a research programme to help to define what their Mediterranean campaign should highlight. The campaigners settled on four issues on which they could back their arguments and actions with documented facts. These were: the quantity and nature of the fishing taking

Campaign for coral
The campaign against coral fishing with the Italian bar began in earnest on 24 May 1986, when the *Sirius* sighted the coral-stripper *Ricomar* at work. The *Ricomar*'s captain at once began to raise the bar, but Greenpeace activists reached the ship in inflatables and clambered onto it (below). The captain then dumped the bar back into the sea, dragging one campaigner under the water. As he was being rescued, another activist took his place on the bar when it re-emerged. The *Ricomar* then abandoned its attempt to gather coral and the action was called off. The Italian bar was banned from Spanish waters late in 1986, but it is still used surreptitiously elsewhere in the Mediterranean.

place in the Mediterranean, and its effect not only on fish but on other marine life; the pollution from industrial, urban and agricultural waste; the threat to wildlife habitats in the sea and on the coasts and islands; and the potentially catastrophic presence of nuclear installations, weapons and waste.

PLUNDERERS OF THE SEA

One of the most destructive forms of 'fishing' in the Mediterranean is that for red coral. Traditionally, divers, or ships using a drag called the 'St Andrew's cross', have taken the coral from the bed of the Mediterranean; but in recent years Spanish and Italian boats had begun to strip the coral by dragging the 'Italian bar' – 6 metres long, 40 centimetres across and weighing over a tonne – across the sea bottom. The bar smashes into the reefs and breaks them up, damaging far more coral than the nets attached to it collect, and destroying everything else alive in its path.

The campaign against the boats using the Italian bar must be one of Greenpeace's speediest successes on record. The first encounter occurred on 24 May, when the *Sirius* came upon the coral stripper *Ricomar* off the island of Alboran between Spain and Morocco, and forced it to abandon its attempt to gather coral. The next action was on land on 22 July, when activists chained themselves to the General Fisheries Secretariat in Madrid, blocked its entrance with an artificial Italian bar, and demanded an end to the coral dragging. At sea, on 7 August, the *Sirius* intercepted an entire fleet of coral-hunting ships and forced them to return to harbour. Meanwhile, political lobbying and publicity had been having their effect, and the Fisheries Secretariat had delayed renewing the coral hunters' licences. Then, on 29 September 1986, the Spanish Minister of Agriculture, Fisheries and Food announced a ban on the use of the Italian bar in Spanish territorial waters, making it illegal on boats operating from Spanish ports. The combination of direct action and unceasing publicity had had their desired effect in just four months.

A disaster in waiting?
Activists from the *Sirius* board the nuclear waste transporter *Mediterranean Shearwater* in Anzio harbour, Italy, on 24 October 1988. The action prevented the ship loading its cargo for nearly two days. The *Mediterranean Shearwater* regularly carries up to 30 tonnes of radioactive waste through the crowded Mediterranean for reprocessing in the UK. If the ship suffered a major fire or collision when fully laden, it would release as much radioactivity as did the Chernobyl disaster of 1986.

PIRATES IN THE MEDITERRANEAN

At the start of summer each year, bluefin tuna come into the Mediterranean from the Atlantic to spawn. Under agreements made through the International Commission for the Conservation of Atlantic Tuna (ICCAT), there is a closed season on tuna fishing as, since 1980, stocks have fallen by 60 percent.

But in June 1988, near the Spanish coast, the *Sirius* came upon a fleet of large fishing boats using longlines to catch tuna. Over 100 kilometres long, each line had between 1,500 and 2,000 hooks. The catches included not merely tuna but sharks and protected sea turtles. The ships, with English and Spanish names, were registered in Venezuela and Honduras – neither of which is a signatory to ICCAT – and ostensibly owned by a Honduran company. These 'pirate' ships change name and registration number overnight and do not show any registration port on their hull.

All of them, however, had formerly belonged to a Japanese company, Foku Toku Maru. The crews were all Korean, Japanese or Taiwanese. In Las Palmas, in the Canaries, Japanese buyers took the ships' catches. And a Japanese government inspection vessel was with the fleet at all times. Greenpeace announced their belief that the ships still ultimately belonged to the Japanese, who were simply sidestepping the law. Other pirate boats operate under Turkish, Sierra Leonese and Panamanian flags, but are owned by Korean and Taiwanese companies.

During the tuna closed season in 1989 the *Sirius* confronted the pirate boats, and on one occasion was nearly rammed. In May 1990 the *Sirius*'s crew boarded a pirate ship in Las Palmas harbour.

Greenpeace recognize that the Mediterranean countries can control fishing only inside their own territorial waters, but persistently ask why these ships, which openly flout international maritime regulations, are allowed to make use of harbours in the western Mediterranean and Canaries. And the organization suggests that one solution to the problem would be an agreement among the Mediterranean countries to extend their national territorial waters so that the whole sea could be adequately policed.

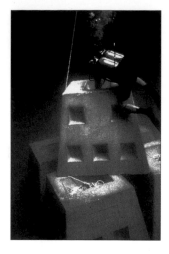

Double indemnity
A diver helps to manoeuvre concrete blocks into position on the seabed to create artificial reefs. The blocks, which Greenpeace laid around the Italian coast, deter illegal trawling by wrecking fishing nets and, at the same time, create a new habitat that encourages fish and plant life.

A protected species?
A Spanish fisherman hauls a loggerhead turtle, which has swallowed the bait on a longline hook, out of the sea. The line will be cut and the turtle put back into the water, but the hook will usually still be embedded in the animal. Half-hearted measures like this conform to the letter of the law that protects turtles, but do little to conserve the turtles' numbers, let alone relieve their suffering.

Trawlers and driftnets

Greenpeace's campaign against inshore trawling not only halted a destructive and illegal practice in some areas of the Mediterranean, but gave a positive boost to the wildlife Greenpeace were trying to protect. Italian and Spanish trawlers used persistently to fish within 5 kilometres of the coast and at depths of less than 50 metres, disturbing fish nursery areas and threatening the *Posidonia* beds that provide such a valuable habitat (see page 89).

The organization's tactics in this case were less to confront trawlers directly than to make it impossible for them to fish in certain waters. In the first action, in May 1986, the *Sirius* dumped 35 artificial reefs — steel drums filled with concrete — in shallow waters east of Malaga, where divers had found evidence of illegal trawling. Any boats fishing in the area would find their nets snagged on the steel bars projecting from the drums, making it impossible for them to continue. Such was the success of this operation that both the Italian and the Spanish authorities began their own artificial reef programmes, installing more sophisticated concrete barriers that deter illegal trawling, but at the same time provide a haven for fish and other marine life.

Fishing with driftnets, too, aroused Greenpeace's ire. These nets can stretch for 40 kilometres through the water and are virtually invisible so they easily ensnare any marine animal that encounters them. The effect has been not only to devastate the stock of fish the nets are intended to catch, but to threaten other species, too. Sea turtles and seabirds also get trapped, while between 1986 and 1989 at least 23 sperm whales drowned in driftnets. In 1989 Greenpeace estimated that the 800 Italian boats using the nets were catching almost 4,000 small cetaceans every year.

Greenpeace began a campaign against driftnetters in Italy in 1988, and against the Spanish boats in 1989. A typical Greenpeace action in 1989 saw the organization in alliance with Spanish longline fishermen, angry that the continued use of driftnets was threatening their own livelihoods. On 10 July the *Sirius* and 40 Spanish longline boats sailed together into Cartagena to proclaim loudly their objection to the illegal fishing.

The campaign bore fruit in 1990. In July, the Italian government declared a ban on the nets and agreed to compensate the fishermen so that they could re-equip their boats with less destructive gear. In October, the Spanish government banned the use of driftnets by ships bearing the Spanish flag and by any ship of any nationality in Spanish waters. But, as Greenpeace point out, the real results will come only when all of the Mediterranean countries introduce a ban on driftnets. Efforts in this direction are made by various international bodies but, so far, with only partial practical results. Following Greenpeace's campaign, countries such as Italy, Spain and Algeria are now strongly in support of a total ban on driftnets.

ACTION AGAINST POLLUTION

Between July and September 1990, the bodies of some 250 striped dolphins were washed up along the coasts of Spain and North Africa. The striped dolphin is a creature of the open sea, so the corpses that came ashore were thought to be but a fraction of the total dead. Scientists estimated that as many as 6,000 dolphins may have died.

Greenpeace reacted by channelling funds to the University of Barcelona to investigate the cause of the deaths, and alerted the Spanish National Institute for Nature Conservation and the regional governments. The environmental research vessel *Toftevaag*, under charter to Greenpeace, assisted the *Sirius* in monitoring the dolphin populations on the high seas, while on land a fleet of vans began collecting corpses, which were then held in cold storage.

Greenpeace's work helped to spur official institutions into action, and in September 1990, scientists, government officials and members of Greenpeace met to co-ordinate efforts. Research has since revealed that many of the dolphins were infected with a virus similar to the one that precipitated the death of thousands of North Sea harbour seals in 1988; in addition, all of the dolphins examined had liver damage characteristic of chemical poisoning.

It is likely to be very difficult to unravel all the causes of this die-off. However, it is known that many synthetic compounds that accumulate in Mediterranean marine mammals do strongly suppress the immune system in other species. As the animals become sick and unable to feed, they draw on the energy reserves in their blubber, which is where most of the accumulated pollutants also reside. Fat 'mobilization', therefore, leads to the rapid release into the bloodstream of comparatively large amounts of substances such as PCBs and DDT – which could further attack the animals' immune systems and livers. In the Mediterranean dolphins, levels of PCBs were as high as 500 parts per million (one dolphin had levels as high as 2,800 ppm), making them among the most highly contaminated mammals in the world. Under the slogan 'Zero 2000', Greenpeace have called for a complete halt to toxic discharges into the Mediterranean by the end of the century.

The waste of industry

The level of pollutants found in the dolphins was a dramatic illustration of the threat that, Greenpeace have long insisted, faces the Mediterranean. From the very beginning of the Mediterranean campaign in 1986, the organization had focused on the issue of pollution and toxic wastes. One of the first targets was the company Tioxide SA, which was dumping 1,000 tonnes of titanium dioxide waste near the entrance to the sea every day.

The firm's sister companies in northern Europe were simultaneously being pressured by Greenpeace for dumping titanium dioxide waste in the North Sea. The chemical had replaced poisonous lead additives in paint since the 1960s; but the process used to extract titanium dioxide from its ore was largely inefficient, and nearly a quarter of the waste consisted of sulphuric acid. This was bad enough, but scientists had also found harmful effects on fish living in the North Sea dumping grounds, which were due to the high proportion of ferrous sulphate in the titanium dioxide waste.

On 13 August 1986 the *Sirius* first went into action against a Tioxide dump ship, the *Nerva*, in the Gulf of Cadiz. Inflatables took volunteers to the ship, where they chained themselves to the discharge pipes and valves to stop them dumping the waste into the sea. After 11 hours, the *Nerva* had no choice but to return to Huelva, the waste – and the protesters – still aboard.

On 15 August, inflatables from the *Sirius* succeeded in putting activists on board both the *Nerva* and its sister ship the *Niebla* after they had attempted to

No place for poisons
Greenpeace activists (above left) block the outflow pipe at the ENCE pulp and paper factory at Huelva, Spain, in June 1989, and (above) block the discharge pipe from the Solvay plastics factory at Rosignano, Italy, in July 1988. Greenpeace had discovered that the output from the Solvay plant had killed all life on the seabed in an area of 10 square kilometres around the pipe, while the level of mercury in the waste was 100 times higher than the legally permitted limit.

OPERATION CETACEANS

In the summer of 1989 Greenpeace Italy sponsored a survey of the small cetaceans in Italian waters – *Operazione Cetacei*. Both scientists and members of the public were involved: led by the chartered research yacht *Highlander*, more than 250 small boats crewed by volunteers joined in the operation, sailing every Saturday in July from harbours in the Italian peninsula, Sardinia and Sicily. Each boat searched a sector of water and noted any sightings of cetaceans.

The survey was invaluable as it gave Greenpeace their first general picture of cetaceans in Italian waters, and particularly of where large numbers lived. The operation also aroused the interest of scientists: a meeting aboard the *Sirius* to discuss the initial results of the census attracted researchers from Tunisia, Algeria and Morocco, as well as Italy and Spain. Over 60

articles appeared in Italian newspapers and magazines over the period of the survey, spreading word of Greenpeace's campaign to ensure the survival of cetaceans in the Mediterranean.

Operazione Cetacei continued the following year; this time Greenpeace France were also involved, and the project focused on the Ligurian Sea, where many dolphins had been seen. Greenpeace's aim was to gather information on the number of species, their breeding and feeding sites, in support of a proposal to make the Ligurian Sea a protected area.

As part of the campaign, Greenpeace intensified their actions against driftnetting, responsible for the deaths of thousands of dolphins every year. The high point of the operation came in July 1990, when driftnetting was banned in Italian waters.

slip out to sea under cover of darkness. Both ships were obliged to return, still fully laden, to port. Actions like these continued in 1987, and were so successful in rousing public opinion that the people of the two Spanish villages Nerva and Niebla asked for the dump ships to be renamed.

At the same time, Greenpeace were meeting with Tioxide to press the company to reduce the waste they dumped and to introduce recycling systems into their plant; they had also formed an alliance with local fishermen and trade unions to try to stop the company's dumping permits being renewed by the authorities. Eventually, in 1987, Tioxide agreed to begin recycling their titanium dioxide waste, gradually reducing the amount they dumped in the sea until, in 1992, dumping would stop completely.

In 1986, Greenpeace had little opportunity to tackle other sources of toxic waste, although in July they drew attention to the poison being poured from the Peñarroya factory into Portman Bay, Murcia (see page 132). And in October, the organization publicly detailed the appalling state of the Huelva estuary after a massive die-off of fish there, the second in five months. Greenpeace pointed to the enormous quantities of toxic waste poured into the Tinto and Odiel rivers by factories along their banks, and dismissed claims that the fish had died of natural causes.

In September 1987, the Andalusian regional government published a plan to reduce the discharge to zero by late 1988. While welcoming the initiative, Greenpeace targeted the ENCE (National Pulp and Paper Mill) plant at Huelva for exemplary action, blocking the company's outflow pipe. In May 1989, Greenpeace announced that samples from the pipe revealed that ENCE were dumping nearly 20 tonnes of waste from chlorinated processes into the river every day, and in June activists again blocked the outlet.

In August 1987 the sailing ship *Greenpeace V* visited the huge petrochemical complex at Tarragona, where a cluster of multinational companies – among them Bayer, Rio Tinto Zinc, Hoescht, Monsanto, Dow Chemical, and BASF – had plants. These had a history of near-disasters, and every day for two decades had been pouring 25,000 tonnes of chemical waste and heavy metals

The best of British
Every day, the UK's tiny enclave on the Rock of Gibraltar throws about 45 tonnes of rubbish off the cliffs and into the sea. In July 1989, Greenpeace volunteers collected a raftful of the garbage, then towed it into Gibraltar harbour and tied it up opposite the Royal Navy's base offices for all to see.

Voyage to nowhere
The *Sirius* mounts a protest against the *Karin B*, carrying toxic waste, in Livorno harbour, Italy. In July 1988, the *Karin B* had collected 167 containers of toxic waste from Koko, Nigeria, where it had been dumped illegally, for shipment back to Ravenna. When the port refused to handle the cargo, the ship changed course, but was subsequently banned from docking in Spain, France, the UK, the Netherlands and West Germany. After 50 days at sea, the crew – many suffering from the effects of fumes from the chemicals – were finally allowed ashore in Livorno. Greenpeace are seeking a ban on trade in all hazardous waste, which is potentially harmful to people and the environment.

THE POISON IN PORTMAN BAY

Probably the most scandalous source of pollution in the Mediterranean was the Peñarroya company's factory in Portman Bay, Murcia, in southeastern Spain.

Every day for nearly 30 years the Portman plant spewed 7,000 tonnes of toxic mud into the bay. By the late 1980s the bay, where once boats of 5 metres' draught could sail, had become a solid mass of poisonous mud. Roughly 50 million tonnes of waste laden with cadmium, lead, zinc, cyanide and sulphuric acid had been deposited in that time, and the continental shelf for tens of kilometres around the bay was utterly devoid of life.

The opening move
Greenpeace first tackled the appalling condition of Portman Bay, into which the Peñarroya company was discharging toxic waste, in July 1986, when activists tried to plug the outflow pipe – with spectacular results. The high mud banks seen here supporting the pipe consist of three decades' worth of poisons.

Greenpeace first moved against the plant very early in the Mediterranean campaign, at the end of July 1986. After warning the factory of their intention, six Greenpeace volunteers from the *Sirius* attempted to block the discharge pipe, and three of them chained themselves to it to stop anyone removing the bung. In fact, the activists did not entirely stop the flow – so that a spray of effluent shot 30 metres into the air as pressure built up behind the bung, making a picture that illustrated better than anything the filth that Peñarroya was pouring into the sea.

In June 1987 Greenpeace exposed the hypocrisy of the Spanish government by dumping a tonne of toxic mud from Portman on the steps of the Ministry of Public Works in Madrid while, inside the building, the minister was celebrating 'World Day for the Environment' with the press. The organization followed up this action with others and, at the end of the year, began legal proceedings against the company. Local fishermen and townspeople joined the campaign with direct actions of their own.

Finally, Peñarroya abandoned the plant, selling the site and the contaminated bay to a tourist development company that intends to build houses and a golf course there. On 1 April 1990, the Spanish General Secretary of the Environment ceremonially halted the discharge from the pipe.

Greenpeace regard the issue as won for all practical purposes – but they are still pursuing the Peñarroya company in the courts in the hope of making them pay for the untold damage they caused the Mediterranean during their time at Portman Bay.

into the sea. Greenpeace exposed the abuse to the public, and in May 1988 made detailed suggestions for how the companies could radically reduce their waste. At the same time the *Sirius* sent divers to take samples from the waste outlets, to establish which companies to target for direct action.

Pigs and pesticides

In Italy, Greenpeace had focused on the effects of nutrients and other pollution entering the Adriatic Sea from the River Po. Alerted by massive blooms of algae in the sea, in 1989 the *Sirius*, accompanied by the oceanographic vessel *Daphne II*, began a well-publicized sampling exercise of waters around the mouth of the Po.

Armed with this evidence, and research indicating that 45 percent of the nutrient pollution in the Adriatic comes from intensive animal farming, Greenpeace decided to target the huge pig farms in the Po valley for action in 1990. On 11 April, for instance, volunteers hung banners on the roof of a giant farm in the Comacchio valley that houses 26,000 pigs – which produce as much 'fertilizer' as about 172,000 people might in a year.

The following month, Greenpeace targeted the Oxon plant in Mezzana Bigli, Lombardy, which produces 12,000 tonnes of highly toxic pesticides every year – and exports nearly 80 percent of these to Eastern Europe. At least one of the herbicides, atrazine, has been confirmed as carcinogenic in laboratory experiments. A group of 11 Greenpeace activists climbed the two solvent recovery towers at the plant and from them hung a huge protest

The suffering Adriatic
The waters of the river Po carry huge amounts of pollutants into the Adriatic Sea, including massive quantities of sewage from the intensive animal farms in the Po valley as well as pesticides and herbicides that the rain washes from farmland. To add to the problems, contaminated sludge dredged from harbours on the Adriatic are dumped in open waters. Greenpeace's Mediterranean campaign has mounted actions against all these sources of pollution: at the giant pig farm in the Comacchio valley (below left), against the dredgers in Ravenna harbour (bottom left) – both in April 1990 – and against the Oxon pesticides plant in Lombardy, in May 1990 (below).

banner. The action ended after a meeting with the managers of the plant at which Greenpeace voiced their demands that production and export of atrazine be stopped immediately and that the company publish information relating to the poisonous nature of all the pesticides they produced.

HABITATS UNDER THREAT

From 1986 Greenpeace drew attention to two particularly glaring examples of places where human activity was in danger of destroying the refuges of protected species – some of them unique in the Mediterranean. One was the Columbretes islands, just east of Castellon, the other (see opposite) was the archipelago of Cabrera off Majorca.

Tourists had been the worst offenders against Columbretes. As a result of human intrusion, plants and animals not indigenous to the archipelago had displaced native species, while tourists and yachtsmen had treated the islands as a rubbish dump. Greenpeace's campaign for Columbretes was brief and effective. In July 1986, volunteers collected a tonne of garbage from the islands and dumped the lot outside the palace of the regional government in Valencia, blocking its doors during a government meeting. In December 1986, the Valencia government declared Columbretes a 'natural park' and announced plans to clean up the islands, control the influx of visitors and restore the local wildlife. Annually since then, despite being harassed by the Spanish navy, Greenpeace have monitored progress on Columbretes. Recently, the park has been extended to include a marine reserve around the islands.

A NUCLEAR-FREE SEA

The entire Mediterranean now exists in the shadow of the nuclear threat – from the four nuclear arsenals and nuclear-powered ships of the French,

A clean sweep
Volunteers (above) collect rubbish left by careless visitors to the Columbretes islands, Spain, in July 1986.

The watchers watched
In June 1988 the Greenpeace flagship *Sirius* chanced on a flotilla of Soviet warships, watched over by a US frigate, carrying nuclear arms, in the Gulf of Hammamet off Tunisia. Over 500 Soviet and US nuclear warheads are always at sea in the Mediterranean.

THE BATTLE FOR CABRERA

The small archipelago of Cabrera, south of Majorca, is a refuge for several endangered species: among the birds, the rarest is Audouin's gull, and others include Eleonora's falcon and the fish eagle. Here too was the last shelter in the Balearics of the Mediterranean monk seal, last seen on the islands in 1977.

None of this meant much to the Spanish military, which in 1973 began to use the islands for their manoeuvres. Several times a year, 1,500 men, with heavy vehicles and artillery, arrived to bombard the archipelago with 500 tonnes of munitions. Navy ships used the islands in their target practice, and in some years the air force too joined in the bombardment.

Greenpeace's aim – supported by scientists, the World Wide Fund for Nature, regional environmental organizations such as the Balearic Ornithology Group, and the public – was to have Cabrera declared a national park, so ending the destruction and offering total protection to the wildlife there.

The organization's first move, in June 1986, was to telegraph the Spanish Minister of Defence to object to the impending manoeuvres – and this made front-page news. After the *Sirius* anchored in Cabrera's natural harbour, interrupting the manoeuvres, the Spanish government agreed to suspend military activity on the islands until an enquiry had established the exact nature of the damage being done.

The Cabrera archipelago, in the Balearics, seen from the air.

But the next September saw troops and equipment embarking at Palma for Cabrera. Volunteers from Greenpeace and the Balearic Ornithology Group chained themselves to the ship to delay it.

In November 1987 a demonstration of 5,000 people in Palma, with written support from more than 40 organizations, showed how strong public feeling was over the issue. At about the same time, Greenpeace revealed that the government's own scientists had condemned the manoeuvres and were also pressing for Cabrera to become a national park. Once more the manoeuvres were cancelled and, since then, each time the military have attempted to resume their exercises, Greenpeace have stopped them by their peaceful protest.

Political progress may have been slow, but already Cabrera's wildlife was benefiting from Greenpeace's success in halting military activity there: in just two years, the colony of Audouin's gulls, for example, had doubled in size.

At last, in October 1988, the Balearics declared Cabrera a national park; but the Ministry of Defence continued to battle for its 'right' to open fire at will on the islands' environment. Finally, in September 1990, the Spanish parliament voted unanimously in favour of declaring Cabrera a national terrestrial and maritime park. However, the fact that the military has declared that it still wants to carry out some limited activity in the park is giving environmentalists cause for concern.

Soviet, US and British navies, from the nuclear-armed air forces of those countries, all of which have bases in the region, and from the nuclear programmes of various Middle Eastern countries. The Gulf crisis that began in the summer of 1990 only increased the risks associated with all this potentially devastating hardware.

Greenpeace's first direct action against the military nuclear threat in the Mediterranean came in September 1987, when three inflatables made a brave attempt to stop the nuclear-armed destroyer USS *Comte de Grasse* from docking in Palma harbour. From 1988, actions followed thick and fast. None of the nuclear navies escaped the attentions of Greenpeace's campaigning ships, from the nuclear-powered and nuclear-armed aircraft carrier USS *Dwight D. Eisenhower* and the French carrier *Foch* — both of which violated Spanish law by bringing nuclear weapons into Spanish harbours — to the British navy's submarine base at Gibraltar.

One of the more intriguing discoveries of the campaign was the anchorage in the Gulf of Hammamet, 35 kilometres off the Tunisian coast, where in June 1988 the *Sirius* came upon five Soviet nuclear warships hove to in mid-ocean — a reflection of the USSR's lack of naval bases in the sea — along with a nuclear-armed US frigate, which was apparently keeping a watching eye on the Soviet flotilla. Volunteers promptly went into action against both navies, and succeeded in painting the international radiation symbol on the Soviet aircraft carrier *Baku* and on the US frigate *Thomas C. Hart*, despite being buzzed by a Soviet launch and sprayed by American fire hoses.

In the same month Greenpeace volunteers staged the organization's first action in the US submarine base at La Maddalena, Sardinia, against the presence of nuclear cruise missiles. Both the Italian and US governments had publicly denied the missiles were at La Maddalena, although the tenders serving the base had been specially re-equipped to carry them three years previously. Greenpeace believed that at least 90 cruise missiles were handled

Confrontation with a giant
Greenpeace inflatables are dwarfed by the aircraft carrier USS *Dwight D. Eisenhower* (above) as they greet its entrance into Palma harbour, Majorca, on 9 June 1988. The giant warship is powered by two nuclear reactors and routinely carries as many as 100 nuclear bombs for its aircraft and up to 50 nuclear anti-submarine depth charges.

Cruising the Mediterranean
Mockingly decked out as a yellow submarine, a Greenpeace inflatable (left) meets a barrage of water from the USS *Frank Cable* and a supporting fire tender during a demonstration at the American submarine base at La Maddalena, Sardinia.

by the base between 1986 and 1988. In addition, samples of the seabed showed a higher level of radioactivity than is normal in the area, which could only have come from the American submarines.

There were two more actions at the base in 1989. Then in February 1990 the Italian parliamentary group for foreign affairs approved Greenpeace's resolution calling for the publication of all data on the radioactivity at La Maddalena – thus acknowledging the nuclear presence for the first time.

SPREADING THE WORD

Greenpeace's successes in the Mediterranean by the end of 1990 had been profound in their effect. Not least had been the increasing awareness – largely through headline-making direct actions – throughout the region of the urgency of the environmental issues affecting the sea. The Greenpeace office in France had been revived; the *Sirius* had received an enthusiastic reception on much of its tour of North Africa in 1989 and when it visited Malta during 1988–1990 and Cyprus in 1990; plans to open a new office in Greece were all but complete – all these things lent hope to the future.

Greenpeace France had collapsed after the bombing of the *Rainbow Warrior* in New Zealand in July 1985, as national interest dominated environmental concern. But in February 1989 the climate was such that the office could reopen. Public membership then was just a few hundred; in the course of 1990, some 23,000 people supported Greenpeace France by their donations.

The revitalized French connection within Greenpeace, and the growing awareness of environmental issues throughout France, should be regarded as

particularly significant in view of the European Commission's determination
to apply the standards of cleanliness it has set for the North Sea to the
Mediterranean by 1992. Greenpeace France have already made their presence
felt in the Mediterranean campaign, publishing a detailed report on pollution
in the Rhône, which contributes to the contamination of the Mediterranean,
and identifying the organizations responsible, and acting against the chemicals
company Rhône-Poulenc in July 1990, when volunteers blocked discharge
pipes and strung a 40-metre satirical banner outside the company's plant.

Into Africa

One of the more delicate tasks the Greenpeace Mediterranean campaign set
itself for the late 1980s was to make its aims known in North Africa. There
were two major problems to face. First, there was the possibility of an
unsympathetic reaction to what is still widely perceived as a 'Western'
organization from peoples who until recently had been colonized by
European countries. Second, the political realities of North Africa are quite
different from those of Western Europe, and the concept of disinterested and
impartial non-governmental organizations is not a familiar one.

   In October 1989, when the *Sirius* set sail from Alicante for a five-week tour
of ports in Tunisia, Algeria and Morocco – three of the 'Maghreb' states – its
aims were accordingly modest: to let people, and governments, know as
neutrally as possible about Greenpeace and their aims, and to discover what
environmental problems there were in the region and attitudes towards them,
so that Greenpeace could formulate appropriate responses to them.

   The tour exceeded all expectations, with local officials, schools, scientists,
journalists and ordinary people eager to hear Greenpeace's message, visit the
ship and bear off publicity material, in every port the *Sirius* visited in Tunisia
and Algeria. In Morocco, the authorities were distinctly cautious, and contacts

were restricted largely to officials (in Tangiers the ship was ignored by all but the police). But it was clear that the potential, at least, existed for developing Greenpeace's activities in this part of the Mediterranean.

The Greek influence

Early in 1991, the organization's most important new move in the region was to open their first office in Greece. Athenians are already well aware of the polluted air that chokes their city, thanks to the plethora of automobiles and the output from local industry. And few Greek cities treat their sewage before dumping it into the sea. For Greece as a whole, agriculture poses a major threat to the Mediterranean, from fertilizers and pesticides and from olive oil processing plants. The contamination of Greek waters by oil is particularly severe – and it is this issue that the Greek office has adopted as its first campaign. To environmentalists, Greece also represents a crucial stepping stone to greater influence in the eastern Mediterranean.

In a region as culturally diverse and as politically unpredictable as the Mediterranean, Greenpeace have had an impact that is far out of proportion to their size and resources in the years since their campaign on behalf of the sea began in 1986. There have been major successes in Spain and Italy. The new Greek office promises to help to spread the organization's message beyond western Europe. Two countries of the Maghreb, at least, are receptive to Greenpeace's aims and methods. There is, then, still hope for the Mediterranean, although one overriding need remains – to make the deeds of the countries of the region match their fine words and good intentions. Few organizations are better placed to drive that message home than Greenpeace.

INDEX

ACKNOWLEDGEMENTS

Our thanks go first to the contributors, whose dedication and expertise is critical to the future of the Mediterranean, and without which this book simply would not have been possible.

Of the many others who helped to create the book in various but always essential ways, special thanks are due to Sofia Alomar, Isabel Fuertes, Carmen Moyano, Teresa Pazos and Maria Luisa Toribio in Spain; Gabriella Guerra, Luca Sabatini and Paolo Vaccari in Italy; and Marjolaine Souquet in France.

Many people too made time to review and comment on the text: grateful thanks to Gianni Squitieri (Italy), Philippe Lequenne (France) and Elias Efthymiopoulos (Greece); to Malcolm MacGarvin in the UK, who was especially generous with his knowledge and advice; and to James Carr, Katharine Clark,

Anne Dingwall, Michael Earle, Lisa Finaldi, Paul Horsman, Bruce Jaildagian, Paul Johnston, Jikkie Jonkman, Andrew Kerr, Jeremy Leggett, Gerd Leipold, Sue Mayer and the UK science unit, Peter Pueschel, Susanna van Rose, Lesley Scheele, Mark Simmonds, Beverley Thorpe, Kay Treakle and Ricardo Wilson-Grau.

John Goldblatt and Liz Somerville gave invaluable help with photographs, as did Sarah Arenson, Mike Coles, Andrew Neal, and the Explorer photographic agency in Paris, whose support in this project we gratefully acknowledge.

We are also especially grateful to John Brookesmith and Julie Whitaker who provided translations of some of the text; to Peter Brookesmith for his help with editing; and to Ian Whitelaw for reading through the final text.

XAVIER PASTOR AND LESLEY RILEY

BIBLIOGRAPHY

Arensun, Sarah, *The Encircled Sea*, Constable (London), 1990.
Arkin, William M., *The Nuclear Arms Race at Sea*, Neptune Papers 1, Greenpeace/Institute for Policy Studies (Washington), 1987.
Arkin, William M., and Handler, Joshua, *Naval Accidents 1945-1988*, Neptune Papers 3, Greenpeace/Institute for Policy Studies (Washington), 1989.
Attenborough, David, *The First Eden*, Collins (London), 1987.
Blake, Gerald H., Dewdney, John C. and Mitchell, Jonathan, *The Cambridge Atlas of the Middle East and North Africa*, Cambridge University Press (Cambridge), 1987.
Braudel, Fernand, *The Mediterranean and the Mediterranean World*, Fontana (London), 1986
Clark, R.B. *Marine Pollution*, Oxford Science Publications (Oxford), 1989.
Goulde, Andrew, *The Human Impact on the Natural Environment*, Blackwell (Oxford), 1990.
Grenon, Michel and Batisse, Michel (eds), *Futures for the Mediterranean Basin: The Blue Plan*, Oxford University Press (Oxford), 1990.
Groombridge, Brian, 'Marine Turtles in the Mediterranean', Council of Europe (Strasbourg), 1988
Haas, Peter M., *Saving the Mediterranean*, Columbia University Press (New York), 1990.
Hinrichsen, Don, *Our Common Seas*, Earthscan (London), 1990.
Holmes, Andrew, 'Electricity in Europe', Financial Times Management.
Kuwabara, Sachiko, *The Protection of the Mediterranean against Pollution from Land-based Sources*, Tycooly International Publishing Ltd (Dublin), 1984
Leggett, Jeremy (ed.) *Global Warming: The Greenpeace Report*, Oxford University Press (Oxford), 1990.
Marchessaux, Didier, 'The Biology, Status and Conservation of the Monk Seal', Council of Europe (Strasbourg), 1989.
Margalef, Ramon (ed.), *Western Mediterranean*, IUCN/Pergamon (Oxford), 1985.
Moberg, Asa, *Nuclear Power in Crisis*, 1986.
Patterson, Walter C., *Nuclear Power*, Penguin (London), 1986.
Raine, Pete, *Mediterranean Wildlife*, Harrap Columbus (London), 1990.
Sainsbury, John C., *Commercial Fishing Methods*, Fishing News Books, (Farnham), 1986.
Stachowitsch, Michael, 'Mass Mortality in the Gulf of Trieste: The Course of Community Destruction', in *Marine Ecology 5 (3)*, Paul Parey Scientific Publishers (Berlin and Hamburg), 1984.
Stachowitsch, Michael, 'Mucus Aggregates in the Adriatic Sea', in *Marine Ecology 11 (4)*, Paul Parey Scientific Publishers (Berlin and Hamburg), 1990.
Toke, Dave, *Green Energy*, Merlin Press (London), 1990.
Tortonese, E. *Fauna d'Italia, Vols X and XI*, Ed. Calderini, 1970.
'Directory of Marine and Coastal Protected Areas in the Mediterranean Region', MAP Technical Reports Series No 26, UNEP (Athens), 1989.
Directory of Wetlands of International Importance, Ramsar Convention Bureau (Gland, Switzerland), 1990.
FAO Fisheries Report, No 426 presented at the Seventh Session of the Committee on Resource Management, Livorno, Italy, February 1989.
High and Dry: Mediterranean Climate in the 21st Century, UNEP (Athens), 1989.
'La Pollution du Rhône', Greenpeace (Paris), 1990.
Papers presented at the joint meeting GFCM/ICCAT: Expert Consultation on Evaluation of Stocks of Large Pelagic Fishes in the Mediterranean Area, Bari, Italy, June 1990.
'State of the Mediterranean Marine Environment', MAP Technical Reports Series No 28, UNEP (Athens), 1989.

ILLUSTRATION ACKNOWLEDGEMENTS

The illustrations on pages 30, 47, 73 and 85 were drawn by **David Ashby**; on page 69 by **Anthony Duke**; and on page 84 by **Sandra Pond**.
The **maps** on pages 20-21, 48-49 and 66 were drawn by **Malcolm MacGarvin**. The representation of the sea in the map on pages 48-49 was based on information obtained by NASA's Nimbus 7 research satellite, processed by Gene Feldman, NASA Goddard Space Flight Center.

PHOTO ACKNOWLEDGEMENTS

Ace Photo Agency: Steve Parker 64-65; **Aquila Photographics:** P. Harris 19 top left; **Ardea London:** Ake Lindau 18 bottom left, Beames 49 top, R.T. Smith 53 top; **Associated Press** 68 top; **Henry Ausloos** 98; **Francesc Avella** 115 bottom, 122 top; **Mario Ayús** 92-93 top; **Bavaria Bildagentur GmbH:** Marcella Pedone 83 bottom; **Bilderling:** Klaus D. Francke 71 right, Ellerbrock & Schafft 93 bottom; **Bios:** A. Pons 64 top; **Nick Birch** 103, 105 bottom; **Werner Braun** 57, 70, 81 top; **Camera Press:** J. Messerschmidt 56; **J. Allan Cash Photolibrary:** 50 bottom right, 65 top right, 107 top right; **Kostas Christou** 99 top left, 99 bottom; **Bruce Coleman Ltd:** Kim Taylor 13 top left, Frieder Sauer 27 top right, Francisco Futil 54 left, Fritz Prenzel 61 top, Michael Freeman 94 bottom; **Mike Coles** 11 top, 86 top, 112-113, 116 top; **Sylvia Cordaiy Photo Library:** Richard Ellis 67 left, M. Smith 76 top left, Eva Miessler 105 top left, Nicholas Farrington 121; **Mario Damato** 63; **Zoran Dragoljevic** 105 top right; **Jerry Edmanson** 51 bottom, 118 right; **Mark Edwards/Still Pictures:** 30-41, 59 top; **Explorer:** G. Boutin 48, D.P.A. 49 centre, José Dupont 51 top, Paul Wysoki 110-111, F. Jourdan 122-123, C. Delu 123 top; **Geoscience Features Picture Library:** Roger Parker 11b; **Geospace, Austria** 28-29; **Courtesy of GOB** 135; **Greenpeace:** Mike Midgley 44 bottom, 46, 49 bottom, Gremo 52, Mike Midgley 53 bottom, 54 left, 65 top left, 67 right, 75 top, 82 top, Culley 82 bottom, Mike Midgley 108 top, Bruno Baltzer 113 top, Mike Midgley 114 right, 117 right, 118 left, 124-125, Dorreboom 126, Mike Midgley 127, Claudio Serangeli 128 top, Morgan 128 bottom, 129 top, Mike Midgley 129 bottom, Morgan 130 top left, Gremo 130 top right, Morgan 131, Dorreboom 132 bottom, Ferraris 133 top left, 133 right, Dorreboom 134 top, Morgan 134 bottom, 135 bottom left, 136 bottom, Gremo 136-137, Smith 138, Mike Midgley 139; **Robert Harding Picture Library:** Brian Hawkes 19 bottom, Walter Rawlings 27 top left, John G. Ross 114 left; **Hutchison Library:** Bernard Régent 72 bottom, Dave Brinicombe 104-105, Liba Taylor 107 top left; **Anton Imeson** 76 bottom; **Impact Photos:** Caroline Penn 23, Roger Scruton 64 bottom left, Colin Jones 106-107; **Jacana:** Sophie de Wilde 6-7, C. Carre 12b, Winner 13 top right, Sophie de Wilde 14 top, K. Amsler 14 bottom, Labat/Lanceau Aquarium de la Rochelle 15 top, Sophie de Wilde 15 bottom right, Varin-Visage 18 bottom right, J.L. Le Moigne 19 top right, François Gohier 55 top, 61 bottom, R. Konig 89 bottom right, K. Amsler 91 top, Guy Morel 101 bottom, K. Amsler 115 top; **Lamont-Doherty Geological Observatory of Columbia University** 21 top; **Frank Lane Picture Agency:** W. Wisniewski 18 top right, B. Borrell 44 top, back cover, Jean Hosking 55 bottom; **Serge Lucas** 83 top, 86 bottom, 90; **M. Mañez, Spain** 99 top right; **Marine Mammal Images:** Thomas Jefferson 60 bottom; Jean-Michel Mille 88; **NASA** 8-10, 75 bottom; **Natural Image:** Bob Gibbons 100-101, Paul Davies 101 top; **Nature Photographers:** J.M. Sutherland/Photonews 1, Hugh Miles 27 bottom, S.C. Bisserot 50 top, J.M. Sutherland 97 right; **Naturofotograferna:** Bo Brännhage 71 left, Tony Holm 96 bottom; **Andrew Neal** 87 bottom; **Network:** Lewis 45 top; **NHPA:** Hellio & Van Ingen 69 bottom, Pierre Petit 77; **Okapia:** Ikan 17 bottom; **Christine Osborne Pictures** 26-27, 79, 80 top, 81 bottom right; **Oxford Scientific Films:** Fredrik Ehrenstrom 17 top, Peter Parks 17 centre left, Godfrey Merlen 60 top, Stephen Mills 80 bottom, Len Zell 96 top, Raymond Blythe 117 left; **Panda Photo:** L. Sonnino Sorisio 16 top, F.D. Domenico 16 bottom, E. Coppola & A. Petretti 122 bottom; **Parc National De Port-Cros:** Robert 17 centre right, 89 bottom left; **PictureBank Photo Library** 95 bottom; **Pitch:** G. Vienne/F. Bel front cover, 101 centre; **Planet Earth Pictures:** David Maitland 13 bottom, Doug Perrine 81 bottom left, Christian Pétron 89 top, 91 bottom, Dick Clarke 97 left; **Popperfoto** 68 bottom; **Rex Features:** © SIPA-Press/ Malanca 87 top, 109, © SIPA-Press/Olimpia 132 top; **Marjan Richter** 12 top, 15 centre left, 15 bottom left; **Spectrum Colour Library** 108-109 bottom, 119 bottom; **Frank Spooner Pictures:** Stefano Nicozzi 72 top; **Michael Stachowitsch** 42; **Stief Pictures:** Sergio Montanari 43, 45 bottom; Duby Tal & Mons Haramati 74; **Viewfinder** 2-3, 22, 24, 92 bottom, 94-95, 122 centre; **Wildlife Matters:** John Feltwell 73; **WWF:** Hartmut Jungius 76 top right.